THE REPTILES AND AMPHIBIANS OF DORSET

David C. Wareham

In memory of
Colin George Wareham
28 October 1918 - 30 October 2007

The British Herpetological Society gratefully acknowledge
the donation of this book by David Wareham.
All proceeds resulting from the sales of this book will be used in the
conservation efforts of the Society in pursuance of its Aims.

Published by
The British Herpetological Society
c/o Zoological Scoiety of London
Regent's Park
London
NW1 4RY

www.thebhs.org

ISBN 978-0-9507371-6-4

CONTENTS

Foreword

The county of Dorset has always been close to my heart, the very word bringing back memories of halcyon days spent searching for reptiles on its threatened southern heaths and along its, then, abandoned railway lines. Dorset to me, means catching the train or riding down to the coast on my old Triumph Bonneville, setting up my tent, eating a hurried meal, and getting out there, before the snakes and lizards give up waiting for my annual visit and disappear back into their winter dens.

Nowhere else in Britain stirs me as much as the thought of a trip to the Isle of Purbeck, in reality a peninsular once almost completely isolated from the mainland by impassable wetlands. Is it just a coincidence that the man writing the book on Dorset's herpetofauna should bear the same name as the town of Wareham, which acts as the gateway to the county's amphibian and reptile rich Purbecks. Or could this book be as much a gateway, introducing the newly enthused or simply the mildly interested, to the marvels of herping in the United Kingdom (by herping I mean looking, not touching, for remember, most of these species are protected).

This is the one place in the UK where I have found all six indigenous reptiles in one day, and in almost tropical numbers. In less than two days we counted 100+ common lizards, 100+ slow worms, 18 sand lizards, 2 grass snakes, 3 smooth snakes and 36 adders. That compares admirably with some of my more exotic locations: 12 anacondas in one day in the Venezuelan llanos, 32 in a week; 16 golden lanceheads in a few hours on Ihla Queimada Grande off Brazil; 75 sea kraits, of two species, in 48 hours on two islands off New Caledonia; 220 sea snakes off Weipa, Queensland in four nights; and 120 sea snakes in four days and nights on Ashmore and Hibernia Reefs, Western Australia.

Yes, for me Dorset, and Purbeck in particular, is a very special place, so it gives me great pleasure to write the foreword to David C. Wareham's *Reptiles and Amphibians of Dorset* in the hope that others will find fascination in the reptiles and amphibians, as well as the other fauna, flora and geology of this unique part of our country. Furthermore, although the main drive of the book is Dorset, this volume could be equally useful in other southern counties, even those lacking natterjack toads, sand lizards and smooth snakes, or even for that matter anywhere else in the UK, because the author includes countrywide species' distributions, and the species accounts are just as relevant in other parts of the UK.

And if you see an adder, do stand back and observe this wonderful creature, then walk on and allow it to continue. This, our only venomous snake, is in desperate trouble in other parts of the country, through habitat destruction, alteration and fragmentation, and through active persecution, yet Dorset still possesses good populations. It is not a crime to be an adder, in fact it would be a fairly inefficient slayer having killed only 12 people in the entire twentieth century (compare that with horses, dogs, cattle, and bees and wasps, for example) so it is much better to reach for your camera than a cudgel.

Mark O'Shea

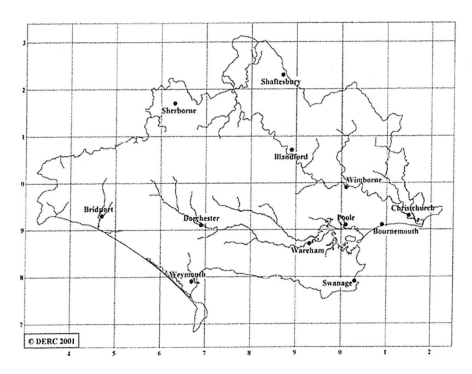

Major Dorset towns

Author's Preface

Approximately 8000 species of reptile and some 6140 species of amphibian are known to exist today and there is no doubt that many more are awaiting discovery. Found in their greatest number and variety in and around the tropics they gradually decrease in quantity as one moves away from the equator into the more temperate zones. Here, in the British Isles for example, it has been traditionally accepted that we have just twelve indigenous species: six reptiles and six amphibians. It has recently been suggested however that latest findings by some field workers demonstrate that perhaps another amphibian, the pool frog, should be added to our list of native species. Although it would appear that the last remaining resident population, in the east of England, recently became extinct a re-introduction scheme is currently underway there. Because argument currently continues over whether the pool frog indeed ever was native to the British Isles, and since it is not found in Dorset, its details have not been included in this book.

Dorset, situated in central, southern England, has almost certainly the richest concentration of these animals of any county in the British Isles. Its geographic location, physiography, climate and wide range of habitats support all twelve of our native reptiles and amphibians, as well as a wealth of other animal and plant species, many of them rare or endangered. The county has consequently earned an international reputation and is much visited by both amateur and professional zoologists with an interest in these fascinating and, in some cases, rare animal groups.

Interest in, and sightings of, our reptiles and amphibians, as elusive as they may be, is not restricted entirely to naturalists and zoologists. Anglers, ramblers, farmers, picnickers, tourists, residents and many others are all likely to come across at least one of these animals as they work on, relax in, or travel through Dorset's countryside.

Two or three species are locally quite abundant and can be encountered even in heavily developed areas. As well as the more familiar newts frogs and toads, reptiles such as the slow worm, common lizard and, in some parts, the grass snake and adder turn up in many gardens throughout the region. With new housing creeping slowly across the already rapidly shrinking countryside such meetings between man and reptile, or amphibian, are becoming more commonplace, much to the unwarranted concern of some of the residents.

Some readers will simply want to identify a particular reptile or amphibian they have seen, whilst others may want to find out a little more about the lives of these interesting animals that they share the countryside with. This book has been written with all these people in mind. Certain aspects of their anatomy, biology, ecology and conservation etc, have either been omitted or dealt with only briefly, for these subjects are too large to be covered adequately in a book of this size. Readers interested in learning more can see the list of *Further Reading* at the end of this book.

Because of the continual development of the countryside our reptiles and amphibians, like so many of our wild animals and plants, are rapidly decreasing in numbers. Tragically many are killed each year out of nothing more than ignorance and fear, and at least three species are now in danger of disappearing from our fauna altogether.

With the possible exception of the adder, our only venomous species, they are completely harmless and all are beneficial to us, playing a substantial part in helping to control the hordes of invertebrates and other small animals which continually attack our clothing, food and homes.

More knowledge and a much greater understanding of our reptiles and amphibians is still required if we are to triumph in halting their present decline. Anyone interested in helping with population surveys, field work, site clearance and other projects can obtain further details by contacting the *British Herpetological Society, c/o The Zoological Society of London, Regent's Park, London NW1 4RY* or, alternatively, *the Biological Records Centre, Institute of Terrestrial Ecology, Monks Wood, Abbots Ripton, Huntingdon, Cambs, PE17 2BR.*

Most voluntary sector surveys are now made through county *Amphibian & Reptile Groups'*, usually driven by one or two keen recorders. These groups, known as ARGs, have formed a loose collective under the banner 'ARG UK', details of which can be found on their website www.arg-uk.org. There is also a recently founded Dorset group, the *Dorset Amphibian & Reptile Network* (DARN), which can be contacted via *The Herpetological Conservation Trust, 655A Christchurch Road, Boscombe, Bournemouth BH1 4AP.*

Reptiles and amphibians are as much a part of the British countryside as bluebells, water voles and song thrushes. It will be a sad day indeed if, through thoughtlessness, neglect, ignorance, and indifference, they are allowed to disappear completely from the wild and open places which remain. Newts, frogs and toads, and snakes and lizards, have been present in Dorset and indeed much of Britain, in one form or another, for millions of years and, with help, tolerance and understanding they will, hopefully, be with us for many more years to come.

D. C. W. Dorset, 2008

Acknowledgements

There are a number of people I wish to thank for their invaluable co-operation, help, advice, and suggestions during the preparation of this book. I am especially indebted to Carolyn Steele and Alison Stewart (*Dorset Environmental Records Centre*); Felicity Grant (*European Wildlife Division, Department of the Environment, 1995*); Henry R. Arnold and Professor Nigel Webb (*Centre for Ecology and Hydrology, Dorchester*); Dr Tony Gent (*Chief Executive Officer, The Herpetological Conservation Trust*); Dr Chris Gleed-Owen (*Research and Monitoring Officer, The Herpetological Trust*); Dr Tim Woodfine (*Head of Conservation and Wildlife Management, Marwell Preservation Trust*), Martin Noble (*Forestry Commission*) and Dr Simon Townson, Trevor Rose, and David Bird (*British Herpetological Society*).

I would like also to express my gratitude to all those who were so quick to respond to my request for certain pictures and who were so generous in allowing me to browse their collections of photographs in order to select some for inclusion in this book. Thank you Tony Phelps, Peter Stafford, Brett Lewis, Tim Woodfine, Helen Fearnley, Mikaella Lock, Philip Pote, John Wareham, David Bird, and Chris Gleed-Owen.

My thanks must also go to all the landowners, both public and private, and unfortunately too numerous to mention each by name, who showed such interest in this project and for consenting to me exploring their land in the search for reptiles and amphibians.

The distribution maps were produced by the *Dorset Environmental Records Centre* using the DMAP for Windows software and include data generously provided by *Natural England, The Herpetological Conservation Trust, the British Herpetological Society Conservation Committee*, and Dorset recorder Philip Temple.

Finally, very special thanks must go to my wife, Rita, whose delightful company, continual enthusiasm and, above all, invaluable assistance on numerous field trips, over a period of forty years, has meant so much.

THE DORSET ENVIRONMENT

The County of Dorset contains a remarkable variety of habitats including, amongst others, both coniferous and deciduous woodland, grassland, wet and dry heath, reedbed, saltmarsh, mudflat and sand dune. Because it has such a wide range of habitats it attracts a large and equally diverse flora and fauna.

Not surprisingly therefore, it is difficult to find any part of the county which is not of some importance from a natural history standpoint. Indeed Dorset has many sites of both national and international importance and this is evident in the number of both national and local reserves, and Sites of Special Scientific Interest (SSSIs), which have been established throughout the region. Several places have also gained European status recently and have since been designated as Special Areas of Conservation (SACs) under the EU Species and Habitats Directive.

The Purbeck Heritage Coast project has been awarded the prestigious Council of Europe Diploma for Nature Conservation on more than one occasion acknowledging the hugely successful liaison between, and endeavours of, the reserves, country parks, natural history societies, landowners, businesses, the Army, local councils, and residents. In December 2001 World Heritage Site status was awarded by UNESCO to the Purbeck and East Devon coastline, officially recognising that this beautiful and geologically important 150 km-strip of Jurassic

Hardy's 'blasted heath' may look a barren wasteland but it is home to many species including all six of our native reptiles

Dorset's spectacular coast is being continually shaped by the forces of the wind and sea

coast is one of the world's great natural wonders, ranking alongside the Great Barrier Reef and the Grand Canyon. Many other areas in the county have also been designated as areas of outstanding natural beauty.

The county's most natural feature is the coast as it is being continually shaped by the forces of the wind and the sea. For example, at Studland the sand dunes there have been developing, whilst Hengistbury Head to the east of the county has actually been disappearing by nearly a metre a year.

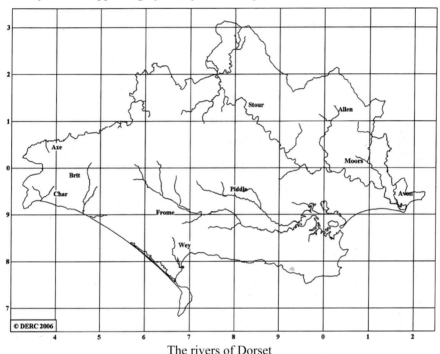

The rivers of Dorset

The coastline from Weymouth to Poole Bay is characterised by sheer cliffs and quiet coves, and features such as Durdle Door and Lulworth Cove are familiar nationwide. The sea life here is rich in both abundance and variety and the coastal path provides easy access to the rugged scenery and fascinating flora and fauna.

Inland, the rolling Wessex Downs form the chalk backbone of Dorset. With their thick hedgerows bordering lush meadows, and small woods of mature oak, hazel and ash, they compose a classical English landscape and an essential network for many kinds of birds, mammals and insects. The steep hillsides are dissected with dry valleys through which wholesome springs bleed into the vale bottoms forming clear, sparkling rivers such as the Piddle and Frome.

Without doubt though the most significant habitat type within the county is the heathland, a characteristic feature of south-east Dorset. Open areas of land

11

Above: The heaths of Dorset with their purple heathers and yellow gorse are some of the finest examples in Europe

Below: Heaths are restricted almost entirely to the north-western coastal fringes of Europe from northern Spain to Norway

with poor, sandy soils, heather, gorse and dwarf shrubs, and a few trees, such heaths are restricted almost entirely to the north-western coastal fringes of Europe from northern Spain to Norway.

The heaths of Britain are among the finest that remain and those of Dorset, with their wide variety of plant and animal species, are particularly important. They lie between the chalk of the Dorset Downs to the north and the Purbeck Ridge to the south, on the gravels, clays and highly acidic sands which surround Poole Harbour and which form the Poole Basin.

Lowland heath in Dorset, and several other southern counties, was once far-reaching, covering over 50,000 hectares. The vast expanse would have been breached only by the river valleys of the Avon, Frome, Stour and Piddle, with their richer soils and lusher plant life. Today less than 8000 hectares of heath remain.

Dorset heathland soils are exceedingly deficient in the minerals upon which plants feed. Rain continually washes these nutrients from the sands to depths which plant roots cannot reach. Waterlogging, which occurs wherever there is clay, causes the development of peat, typical of the bogs and mires found in the valleys and depressions of the county's heathlands. Hard crusts, formed by the deposits of humus and iron in the soil, also prevent drainage.

The dry heaths, wet heaths, and bogs all have communities of plants and

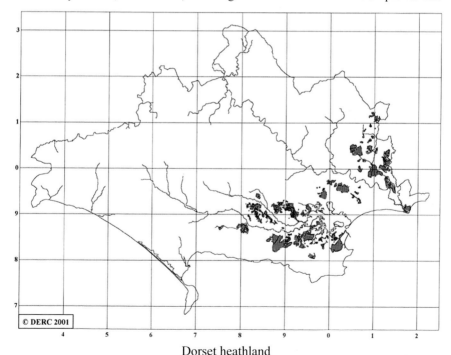

© DERC 2001

Dorset heathland

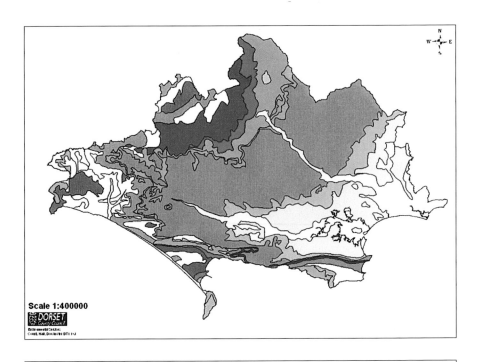

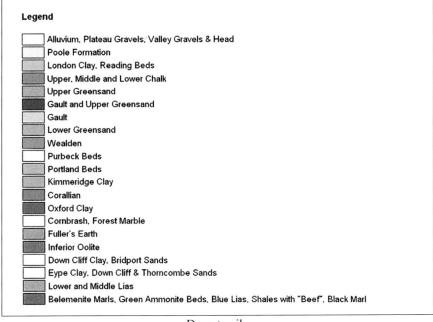

Legend

	Alluvium, Plateau Gravels, Valley Gravels & Head
	Poole Formation
	London Clay, Reading Beds
	Upper, Middle and Lower Chalk
	Upper Greensand
	Gault and Upper Greensand
	Gault
	Lower Greensand
	Wealden
	Purbeck Beds
	Portland Beds
	Kimmeridge Clay
	Corallian
	Oxford Clay
	Cornbrash, Forest Marble
	Fuller's Earth
	Inferior Oolite
	Down Cliff Clay, Bridport Sands
	Eype Clay, Down Cliff & Thorncombe Sands
	Lower and Middle Lias
	Belemenite Marls, Green Ammonite Beds, Blue Lias, Shales with "Beef", Black Marl

Dorset soils

animals specific to each of them. Particularly noted for their populations of reptiles and, to a lesser extent, amphibians are two or three sites which warrant a mention here.

Studland Heath, to the south-east of Poole Harbour, is invaluable as a habitat. Covering almost 650 hectares it forms part of a promontory which extends northwards to Shell Bay at the entrance to the harbour. In 1962 the Studland Heath National Nature Reserve was established and is presently managed and owned by the National Trust.

The reserve there was created not only because of the particularly interesting way in which the sand dunes have developed over the past four hundred years,

At Studland Heath all six of our native reptiles can be seen in one day

but also to help preserve the rapidly disappearing heathland and the rare plants and animals found in the area.

Most of the reserve lies between the Ferry Road and Studland Bay. From suitable places along the road one can see the undulating sand dunes and catch a glimpse of the lake, Little Sea, a dominating aspect of the reserve. Around the edge of the lake are reedbeds and swampy sallow woodland known as 'carr'. There are also drier woodlands and areas of both wet and dry heath. On the eastern side of the lake there are the older dunes now covered with mature heather, birch scrub and gorse, while nearer the beach the younger dunes are covered with heather and grass.

Studland Heath is one of the few places in the whole of the British Isles where all six native reptiles can be seen still in any numbers and, on a favourable

day, it is quite possible, with luck and a stealthy approach, to see specimens of all six species within just a few hours.

The grass snake, slow worm and common lizard can be seen in the more damp areas, such as around the edges of the water-filled shell holes and amongst the swampy carr. The smooth snake and sand lizard on the other hand prefer the drier, heather-clad dunes and heathland, while the adder can be encountered just about anywhere, though usually amongst or close to thick undergrowth.

To the south-east of Studland the chalk downs project into the sea at Handfast Point. Between here and Ballard Point, a kilometre further south, lies Ballard Down towering some 150 metres above the sea. On the gorse-covered, south-facing slopes adders have been so abundant in some summers that notices were once frequently erected alerting the public, many of whom exercised their dogs there. In recent years the adder population there has decreased, much as it has over the country as a whole.

Beyond Swanage one can join the Dorset Coast Path and anywhere, from Durlston Head across the downs and grassy cliffs to East Lulworth, one is likely to see common lizards, slow worms, adders, and the occasional grass snake. Male adders along the route seem to show a particularly wide range of colour: silvery grey, off-white, golden yellow, olive, and reddish brown, but always with the characteristic black markings which in females are always brown or reddish.

Both the adder and common lizard can be observed on warm days basking in the sun amongst the gorse, brambles and bracken, almost anywhere along the cliffs and on the downs but especially in and around the stone and shale-filled

hollows, some of which used to be working quarries. Slow worms, common toads and newts can be found sometimes by carefully turning over some of the many stones and other debris in these places. Whilst it should always be remembered that any animals thus discovered should always be left where they are found and any stones or logs carefully replaced afterwards, it should also be remembered that the greatest care should always be taken when replacing these stones and logs etc, so as not to crush any animals beneath them.

Finally, Arne, a peninsula situated on the western side of Poole Harbour almost 5 kilometres east of the town of Wareham. In 1965 a reserve was established there by the Royal Society for the Protection of Birds, initially by lease. In 1979 the Society was able to purchase not only the leased land but additional areas as well. With further small purchases and a lease of another 33 hectares the reserve now covers over 490 hectares and includes Arne Hill, the highest land for several kilometres.

The sands and gravels laid down during the Tertiary period are covered with a shallow layer of peat which drains freely, is very acid, and deficient in nutrients. The main habitat there is heathland which is dominated by ling *Calluna vulgaris.* Quite large expanses of gorse *Ulex europaeus* grow in and around the combes, whilst Scots pine *Pinus sylvestris* and bracken *Pteridium aquilinum* are obvious features of the reserve.

A number of bog systems drain off into the harbour. In these wet areas *sphagnum* is prominent, gradually giving way to cross-leaved heath *Erica tetralix* and the rare Dorset heath *E. ciliaris.* The saltmarsh, which now covers over 800 hectares, is dominated by cord grass *Spartina anglica*, first recorded in Poole in 1889.

Arne has both deciduous and coniferous woodlands. In the former, silver birch *Betula pendula* predominates although there are small areas of, what appear to be, cultivated beech *Fagus* spp., oak *Quercus robur*, and sweet chestnut *Castanea sativa*. Scattered rowan *Sorbus acuparia*, willow *Salix* spp., and holly *Ilex aquifolium* grow naturally. In the coniferous woodlands the trees are mainly Scots pine and the now commonplace maritime pine *P. pinaster*.

Like Studland, this is one other area which is home to all six of our native reptiles although perhaps not quite in such numbers. The adder is by far the most common of the three snakes, whilst the grass snake on the other hand is less so. Of the amphibians, the palmate newt occurs in a few of the ponds, and both the common frog and common toad turn up from time to time, although not always within the boundary of the reserve itself.

As already stated the sites just discussed are especially noted for their reptile populations. Although the smooth snake and sand lizard are confined mainly to the heaths and reserves, and the natterjack toad currently to just three or four sites in the east of the county where it has been reintroduced, the remaining four reptile and five amphibian species are distributed fairly widely throughout the county of Dorset and can be encountered, in suitable places, just about anywhere.

A typical example of dry heath in the Purbecks

SPECIES ACCOUNTS OF DORSET'S NATIVE REPTILES AND AMPHIBIANS

Amphibians

GREAT CRESTED NEWT – *Triturus cristatus*
(Warty newt)

Identification: The second largest of all the European newt species attaining some 12-15 cm, exceptionally 20 cm. Dark purplish-brown or greyish above with somewhat indistinct rounded dark spots. The sides of the head, flanks and limbs are speckled with iridescent white or silver. Underside is yellow to dark orange or vermilion with grey to black spots or blotches varying in both size and number. The skin is coarse and warty. Throat whitish and usually densely speckled with brown. Toes annulated with yellow and black. The tail has a white or silvery-blue stripe along the middle of each side in the male. The stripe is absent in the female. The yellow to vermilion colour of the belly extends along the lower edge of the tail in both sexes. Iris of the eye is golden yellow.

Male great crested newts develop high toothed crests on their backs.

Photograph: Brett Lewis

In the spring the adult male has a high, toothed crest beginning between the eyes and ending at the base of the tail. The tail is also crested but the denticulations are much less defined. The lower crest of the tail is smooth. Once the breeding season has passed the crest disappears leaving a low ridge. The back of an adult female has a slight depression along its whole length throughout the year. The limbs of the male are longer, in proportion to body length, than those of the female and the tail in both sexes is always shorter than the combined length of the head and body. Albino and partial albino forms can occur, the latter having a harlequin appearance.

This species can produce a faint squeak.

Longevity: The recorded lifespan of this species, in captivity, is 27 years.

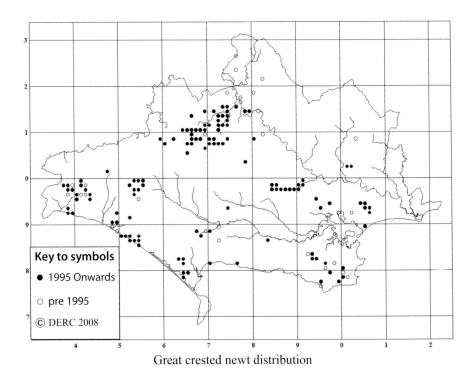

Great crested newt distribution

Dorset range: A local species and apparently absent from many parts. Nevertheless it is distributed quite widely over much of the county although, in some districts, it appears to be restricted to areas of greensand or clay. Outside of the breeding season it may be found over a kilometre from water and, on the Purbeck coast, has been found beneath stones only metres from the cliff edge.

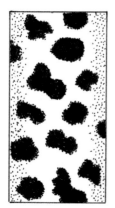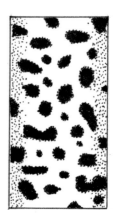

Variations in the ventral pattern of the great crested newt

Distribution in Britain: Widespread over much of Britain but less common in Scotland, Wales and the south-west of England. Absent altogether from Ireland.

Habitat: Sometimes found throughout the year in deep, slow-flowing water of ponds, ditches and watery meadows. Breeding pools are usually of a depth greater than 25 cm, clear and fairly unpolluted, and often situated on chalk or clay soils. Although this species sometimes shares waters with other newt species and sometimes frogs, it is rarely found in those inhabited with toads which tend to prefer deeper water.

Terrestrial individuals may be found in the vicinity of their breeding waters or some distance away in damp places beneath stones, logs or other debris, in dunes, rough pasture, woodland, scrub and arable fields etc. A thick undergrowth containing a variety of shrubs and low-lying plants is an essential requirement for this species, proving not only shelter and a wide variety of invertebrate prey when on land but also a means of dispersing, concealed from predators, into the surrounding countryside from the breeding grounds.

Habits: Adult newts emerge from hibernation in the middle of March and the breeding season begins in late April and early May when the courtship crests of the males have had three or four weeks to develop.

Courtship is not quite so elaborate as that of other newt species. The male follows the female closely, frequently rubbing his snout against her flanks. Raising himself on his legs he arches his back and prevents her from moving away by positioning himself in front of her. His tail twitches and thrashes constantly and occasionally he actually strikes the female with it. Finally he deposits a small packet of sperm beside her which she then moves over drawing it up into her cloaca.

Between 200 and 300 yellow to light green eggs are laid singly, usually in depths of between 30 and 100 cm, on the leaves of submerged aquatic plants. The female carefully wraps each one in a leaf with her hind feet to protect them from predators although some are simply deposited on the pond bottom or amongst submerged detritus.

As soon as the female has laid all her eggs, which are 2.5 mm and, with the capsule, about 4.5 mm in length, both adults move onto the land although they may return to the water several times during the summer if the moisture content of the surrounding terrestrial habitat is inadequate. Hatching of the eggs, which is generally about two or three weeks later, depends not only on temperature but also the absence of a lethal gene which, in Europe, has been responsible for preventing some fifty percent of eggs of this, and closely related species, from hatching.

Newly hatched larvae measure about 15 mm, are transparent, and often swim in open water at various depths. The efts, or 'newtpoles' (immature larvae), feed on microscopic animals such as protozoa and unicellular algae and gradually progress to eating larger animals, such as water fleas and worms, as they grow. The larvae of newts are different from those of frogs and toads in that they are carnivorous and retain external gills until just before metamorphosis. They grow their forelimbs

A courting pair of great crested newts (female above).
Photograph: Brett Lewis

first, a few days after hatching, the hind limbs developing about six weeks later. It is not until they reach 60 to 70 mm, usually by September but sometimes in their second year, that they disperse and move out of the water on to the land.

The great crested newt is sensitive to light and prefers to spend the daylight hours hiding away in rock piles, beneath sheets of corrugated iron, under fallen trees, or in compost heaps etc, emerging at twilight to forage for food. The diet of this species consists of insects and their larvae, small snails, earthworms, and other small invertebrates. Aquatic caddis-fly larvae are devoured in their cases. The tadpoles of frogs and toads are taken and even larvae of their own kind. Large specimens have been known to catch and devour adult smooth newts and baby slow worms. Prey is detected by both sight and smell.

With the onset of winter the newts prepare themselves for hibernation and seek out suitable places in which they can spend the colder months in a state of torpidity. Such places (hibernacula) may include piles of leaves, hollow trees, cellars, holes in walls, and disused rabbit and rodent burrows. As temperatures continue to drop the newts will move further below ground and they have been uncovered at depths of over a metre. Some individuals may actually hibernate in the mud and detritus of their breeding waters. These are generally larvae which have yet to metamorphose and sub-adults which will breed for the first time in the coming spring. Suitable hibernacula for the newts must be damp whilst remaining free of frost throughout the winter. Such sites may not be particularly plentiful in any given area in which case numbers of newts may hibernate together. Groups of several dozen individuals have been encountered and often in the presence of other newt species and sometimes frogs and toads.

The differences between the male and female adult great crested newt cannot usually be detected until their second or third year when sexual maturity is reached. The species is a fast and powerful swimmer moving with the help of the tail alone, the four limbs being held close to the flanks.

SMOOTH NEWT - *Lissotriton* (formerly *Triturus*) *vulgaris*

(Spotted newt; common newt)

Identification: Adults 80 to 97 mm in length but specimens of up to 110 mm have been recorded. The tail accounts for half the total length. Females tend to be somewhat shorter than the males but are usually heavier bodied.

Breeding males are light or dark olive green to brownish above and spotted or peppered with dark green or black. These markings form five stripes on the top and sides of the head, one of them passing through the eye. Spots along the flanks are larger and more rounded. The underside is red, orange or yellow, paler on the sides and on the throat, and spotted with dark green, brown or black. A continuous, undulating crest, up to 10 mm high and tipped with black from the head to the tip of the tail, broad fringes on the toes of the hind feet, a strong ventral pattern and three longitudinal grooves on the head are all characteristic. The lower edge of the tail is generally orange with a light bluish streak above it. Once breeding is over the crest is reduced to a ridge and the toe fringes disappear. On land the skin becomes dry and velvety and the glossy, brightly coloured markings are lost completely.

Females are olive, brown or yellowish-brown above, frequently with small, dark spots which may, in certain individuals, join together to form two parallel lines on the back reaching down onto the tail. On the side of the head there is an indistinct stripe. The underside is the same colour as in the male but paler and with smaller spots. The belly spots of the female vary in number and in some may be

A breeding pair of smooth newts (male above right)

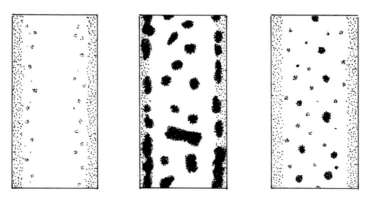

Variations in the ventral pattern of the smooth newt

quite dense whilst in others they are absent. The throat is white with a peppering of dark spots. A low ridge is often present on the back throughout the year. In the breeding season the tail crest is well developed and smooth. The iris of the eye is veined with black and gold.

Longevity: The lifespan of this species, measured in captive individuals, is approximately 18 years.

Dorset range: Fairly widespread throughout the county.

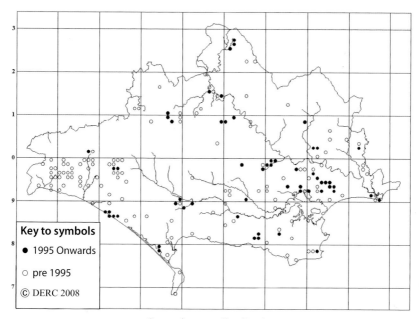

Key to symbols

● 1995 Onwards

○ pre 1995

© DERC 2008

Smooth newt distribution

25

Upper left: A male smooth newt in breeding condition

Lower left: The larvae of newts, unlike those of frogs and toads, bear feathery gills.
Photograph: Peter Stafford

Upper right: A terrestrial non-breeding smooth newt (male)

Lower right: A terrestrial smooth newt (female)

Distribution in Britain: Distributed over most of Britain and is the only newt species found in Ireland. In the extreme north of Scotland and south-west England it is rare or absent and appears to be most numerous in the midlands, east, and south-east England.

Habitat: The smooth newt occurs throughout Dorset in a wide variety of damp situations, beneath stones, logs and other debris, in meadows, marshes, woodlands and gardens etc. Its breeding waters are generally shallow, still, well-vegetated, non-acidic ditches, ponds and canals.

Habits: The habits of the smooth newt are very similar to those of the great crested newt and both have been found in the same waters. The return to the breeding pools begins immediately upon their emergence from hibernation in late February or March, with the males appearing first. Sexual maturity in this species is reached any time between the ages of two and five but usually occurs in the fourth year.

Mating begins in early April. Courtship is similar to that of the great crested newt and during April the male can be observed displaying throughout the day. Courtship and mating is usually finished by the end of May. The female lays several eggs a day in May and June and uses her hind feet to carefully wrap each one in the leaf of an aquatic plant.

The number of eggs laid varies, depending on the age of the female, with 200 or so being laid in the first year of mating and 300 to 400 in a more mature individual. Depending on the temperature the cream-coloured eggs, which are about 1.5 mm in diameter and, with the capsule, about 3 mm long, hatch after two or three weeks. Metamorphosis from larva to newt takes place some nine to twelve weeks later and the young newts leave the water between July and September.

When breeding and egg-laying has been completed the adults generally leave the water. The rest of the summer is then spent in the vicinity of the breeding waters although some individuals may wander some distance from them. During periods of very hot, dry weather the smooth newt may well go into a state of torpor, or aestivation. This is a state of inactivity during which the metabolic processes are greatly reduced. Feeding and other normal activities are resumed once conditions return to normal.

The smooth newt is mainly nocturnal emerging from its daytime shelter at dusk in order to search for food. It is a very active hunter and will pursue and examine anything that moves. Earthworms, small snails, slugs, insects and other invertebrates are snatched up, usually with the tongue. Large adults have caught and devoured baby slow worms. In water prey items are simply snapped up and sucked into the jaws. They may include freshwater shrimps *Daphnia* and insect larvae in their diet and, in the spring, will take frog spawn and, later, tadpoles. They may also eat their own larvae and those of other newts.

Hibernation begins in late October and takes place in disused rabbit warrens and rodent burrows, beneath leaf litter, bark and other debris, and in compost heaps, cellars, mines and caves etc. It is remarkably tolerant of the cold and can endure temperatures as low as 0° C (32° F). Consequently it is not unusual to encounter this species moving around, both in water and on land, during the winter months. Non-metamorphosed larvae will over-winter in the breeding ponds, where they will often be joined by hibernating juveniles and sub-adults.

PALMATE NEWT – *Lissotriton* (formerly *Triturus*) *helveticus*

Identification: This is our smallest newt reaching a length of 75 to 90 mm and exceptionally 100 mm. Its tail accounts for less than half of its total length. In general shape and appearance it is very similar to the smooth newt but there are some differences. The palmate newt lacks any spotting on the throat and, during the breeding season, the male's dorsal crest is a good deal lower and the edge straight and smooth rather than undulating. Consequently this feature is difficult to see when viewing the animal in water. Its tail is sharply truncated at the tip where it continues as a central black filament measuring 4 to 5 mm in length, and the toes of the hind feet are fully webbed and very dark, often contrasting distinctly with the paler muddy bottom of the pond in which it dwells. Both male and female have a prominent ridge down each side of their backs giving the body a square-like look when seen from the front. The smallish, rounded head has three longitudinal grooves, and a dark stripe on each side passing through the eye.

Once the breeding season is over the male's crest is reduced to a low ridge, the webs on the hind feet disappear, and the tail filament is absorbed into the body until just a black point remains. The two ridges on the back also shrink in size, sometimes disappearing completely. The tail of the female is fully developed and does not end in a filament like that of the male.

Male palmate newt. *Photograph: Peter Stafford*

The male palmate newt is light or dark olive green or brown above, speckled or marbled with darker green or brown which may, in some individuals, blend together to form two lines running the length of the back. The underside is pale orange, yellow or golden and thinly spotted or speckled with brown in the centre whilst the outer edge is whitish. The belly colour may extend down the lower edge of the tail which has two rows of prominent dark spots with yellow or light brown in between. The hind feet are dark olive brown to black. The throat is almost always white but may sometimes have a pinkish hue. The iris of the eye is black and gold.

The female is light or dark olive green to brown above, and speckled or marbled with dark green. A dark, dorsolateral line may be evident in some individuals. The underside is the same colour as in the male but the spots are fewer or absent altogether. Two prominent tubercles are also present on the underside of the hind foot.

Longevity: This species, under laboratory conditions, has lived for 19 years.

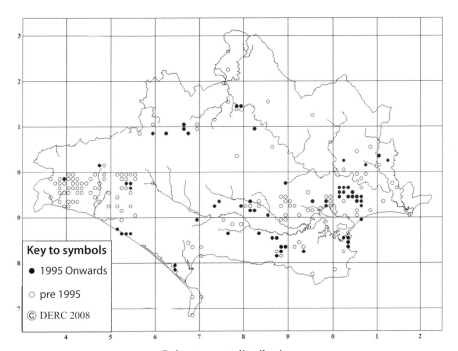

Palmate newt distribution

Dorset range: The palmate newt cannot be called a common species in Dorset but it is nevertheless present at a number of sites, particularly in the west, north, and east of the county where it can be encountered in the acidic pools on the heaths.

 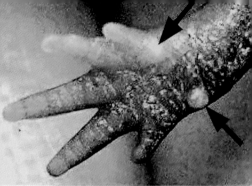

The hind foot of a breeding male palmate newt is webbed.
From a photograph by Peter Stafford

The hind foot of a female palmate newt showing the two tubercules.
Photograph: The HCT

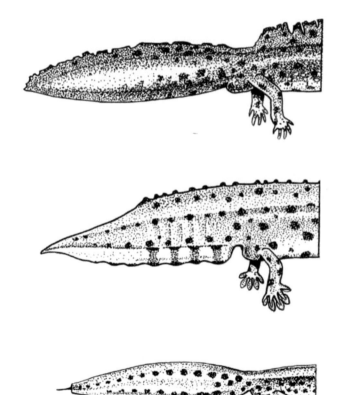

The tails and hind feet of breeding male newts
(From above) great crested, smooth, and palmate newt.

Distribution in Britain: With the exception of the Outer Hebrides the palmate newt is fairly widespread over most of Scotland, England and Wales. It also occurs on the islands of Skokholm and Skomer. It is particularly abundant in the north of Scotland and in the south-west and south-east of England. It is absent from Ireland.

Habitat: Although mainly an upland species it has been found at all levels, in several types of habitat including farmland, marsh, wet grassland, deciduous forest and heath. During the breeding season the species can be encountered in a variety of still or slow-flowing, shallow, mostly acidic waters such as ponds, lakes, canals and brackish coastal pools.

Habits: Probably the most aquatic of our three native species and on high ground it may be found in the water throughout the year. At lower levels however it often leaves the water as soon as the breeding season has come to an end.

Courtship is similar to that of the great crested newt and smooth newt and after mating has taken place, in March and April, the female lays her cream-coloured eggs each measuring about 1.5 mm in diameter and, with the capsule, about 3 mm in length. After they hatch the larvae take some four months to develop and during July and August they metamorphose and emerge on to the land as tiny replicas of the adults, measuring 30 mm in length. The feeding habits and other activities of this species are also similar to those of the two previous species.

Female palmate newt. *Photograph: Peter Stafford*

COMMON FROG - *Rana temporaria*
(Brown frog; grass frog)

Identification: Average length of an adult male (from snout to vent) is approximately 75 to 80 mm, and an adult female 80 to 95 mm. Colour and pattern very variable even in the same individual. Upper parts may be grey, yellow, orange, red, brown or greenish, and spotted or marbled with red, brown or black. The spots may also vary in size, number and shape. Underside is off-white or pale yellow to orange, speckled with grey or brown in the males, and pale yellow to orange, speckled with brown, orange or red in the females. Albino forms sometimes occur and several populations are known from urban areas in the county.

The iris of the eye is a golden yellow speckled with brown and the pupil is horizontal in bright light. The margin of the upper lip is usually light brown or golden in colour. Well-developed skin folds pass down each side of the back and some individuals have a broad, light and indistinct vertebral stripe.

The only markings that remain constant in all but albino individuals are the dark bars on the limbs, the dark streak on the front part of the arm and another in front of the eye, and the distinct elongated patch, or 'mask', on the side of the head including the tympanum. In the breeding season the males are recognised by their strong forelimbs and black nuptial pads on the thumbs, and a bluish tinge particularly on the throat. The females have numerous small, pearly granules on their flanks at this time.

The common frog

The voice of the common frog is a quiet 'krook-krook-krook', soft and rumbling like the purring of a cat, and usually made beneath the water. When attacked by a predator the amphibian can make a loud and sometimes protracted scream similar to that of a distressed rabbit.

Longevity: In captivity a specimen of this species has been recorded as having reached an age of 12 years.

Dorset range: The common frog has a fairly wide distribution throughout the county and, providing the habitat is suitable for its needs, can be found almost anywhere.

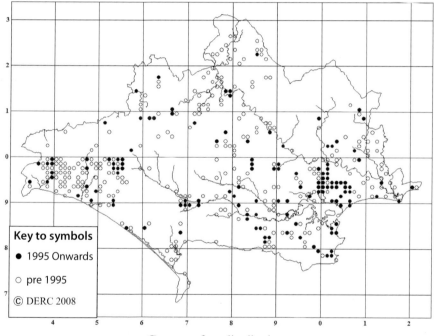

Common frog distribution

Distribution in Britain: Found over the whole of England, Wales and Scotland with the exception of the Outer Hebrides. It occurs in Ireland though its distribution there is somewhat patchy.

Habitat: Damp woodlands, marshes and meadows are this species preferred situations but can turn up just about anywhere including roadside verges, gardens and parks. Often found far from water especially during the summer, but generally in places which provide dampness and shade.

Habits: A fairly solitary species outside the breeding season. Most active in the evening but often seen on the move during the day, particularly during or immediately after a heavy shower, and has been seen basking in bright sunshine. Never very far from cover it seldom has to make more than a few jumps to find a hiding place when threatened or disturbed.

Although sometimes seen crouching in vegetation several centimetres from the ground, the common frog rarely climbs. Hopping and jumping are the usual methods of locomotion when on land. In water it swims well, employing the hind legs only, the forelimbs being held tightly to the sides of the body.

Food consists of a fairly wide variety of small invertebrates including insects, spiders and crustaceans. Snails are a particular favourite and examination of the frog's stomach contents has shown that they form the largest part of its diet in those areas where snails are found.

The common frog emerges from hibernation at the end of February (this may be much earlier in mild winters) and makes its way to the breeding pond. The same ponds are used year after year. Males are usually the first to appear, sometimes by as much as a week or more, and as soon as the females arrive pairing takes place and may last for 48 hours or so. The male grips the female just behind the front legs, in a breeding embrace known as amplexus, and fertilizes the eggs as they are laid.

Each female lays over 1000 eggs in irregular clumps in shallow water and as soon as spawning is over the males and females separate immediately. The hatching of the eggs is dependent upon temperature but generally takes about two weeks. The larvae, or tadpoles, have external gills for only a few days before they develop internal gills, and feed on filamentous algae progressing to more animal based food as they develop. After about five weeks the hind legs develop followed, some seven weeks later, by the forelimbs which break through the skin just prior to metamorphosis. The tadpoles may grow to a length of 45 mm, but the newly metamorphosed frogs are only about 13 mm.

Adults spend the rest of the summer on land but often in the vicinity of the breeding ponds into which they will hurriedly leap if disturbed. They prefer to secrete themselves beneath stones or logs, or in holes and hollows in walls or trees etc, sometimes in the company of newts or toads in regions where the range of these species overlaps. Some of the tadpoles may well remain as such if temperatures are unusually low or if food is in short supply. Those which undergo metamorphosis do so from around June onwards although this may be earlier in some regions.

Hibernation begins in November as a rule but again is entirely dependent upon prevailing temperatures at the time. Many males will winter in the mud at the bottom of the breeding waters be they canals, lakes or garden ponds, while females and juveniles spend their hibernation on land in old rabbit warrens, beneath garden sheds or in cellars, or in hollows amongst the roots of trees etc.

Upper left: A gravid female common frog laden with eggs.
Lower left: Some individuals may exhibit large areas of black.
Upper right: Colour and pattern in the common frog is extremely varaiable.
                     Photograph: John Wareham
Lower right: Black or melanistic specimens are not uncommon in some areas.

COMMON TOAD – *Bufo bufo*

Identification: Heavily built, dry-skinned and warty. Average size of adult males is 65 to 76 mm, whilst females are from 80 to 95 mm. Larger specimens occur from time to time and a colony in east Dorset in 1990 had females to 110 mm and males to 82 mm. Ground colour is brownish varying from sandy grey to brick red, dark brown, grey or olive, usually uniform but sometimes with darker blotches and patches. Underside off-white or grey, often with darker marbling. The adult females and juveniles may have red or orange on their larger warts. The eye is gold or copper and veined with black. The pupil is horizontal in daylight.

The prominent parotoid glands on the sides of the head to the rear of the eyes are slightly oblique. Breeding males have a smoother, shinier skin with a slight greenish tinge and more muscular forearms. The inner three fingers have dark brown or black horny skin on their inner and upper surfaces and are used to help grip the female during spawning. There are no external vocal sacs. The voice of the male is a strong, high-pitched 'kwark-kwark'. Females do not call.

Longevity: One of the longest lived of all our native reptiles and amphibians and, under controlled conditions in captivity, has reached an age in excess of 40 years.

A female common toad

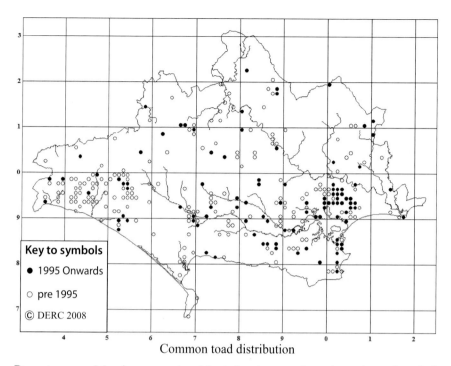

Common toad distribution

Dorset range: May be encountered just about everywhere throughout the whole county but whilst in some areas it may be locally quite common in others it may be rare or absent altogether.

Distribution in Britain: Distributed widely over the whole of England, Wales and Scotland but is absent from Ireland.

Habitat: Can be encountered in a wide variety of habitats including heaths, dunes, woodland, parks and gardens. It is equally at home in damp or dry situations.

Habits: Outside of the breeding season the common toad is solitary and terrestrial. Although it has been observed occasionally basking in warm sunshine it is mainly nocturnal spending the daylight hours hidden away beneath rock piles, fallen trees, rubbish heaps or rotting vegetation etc. It emerges at dusk to forage for food although a heavy shower of rain during the day will sometimes compel it to venture forth.

The homing instinct of the common toad is well known and it will frequently leave its hiding place after dark and travel up to 250 metres before returning again in the early morning. It walks as a rule but will make small hops when suddenly alarmed or disturbed. It is a powerful swimmer and can climb well, sometimes even attempting almost vertical inclines.

When approached by a predator such as snake for example the toad assumes a characteristic defensive posture. Raising its hindquarters and holding its head downwards it inflates its body with air. This makes it look much bigger than it is in reality and is usually, though not always, successful in thwarting such an enemy.

Food basically consists of just about anything it can cram into its mouth. Insects and their larvae, snails, and earthworms are probably the items most frequently taken

The common toad is one of the longest lived
of our native reptiles and amphibians.

but it will also devour smaller amphibians, young reptiles, and baby rodents. Prey is examined closely before being snapped up by the tongue. Sometimes the toad will follow a prey item around for some minutes, watching it intently all the time, before finally catching it. Whilst this inspection is going on the toad's toes on the hind feet flick and twitch in apparent excitement. The forearms and hands are used to assist the entry of the prey into the toad's mouth. When worms are swallowed the toad cleans them of any surplus soil by passing them through two fingers of one or both hands as they are swallowed.

Emergence from hibernation usually occurs in late March or early April although in Dorset it can be as early as February. It has often spent the winter along with many other toads and, consequently, as they all awaken at about the same time they migrate to the breeding ponds in numbers. The same breeding waters are used each

Common toads often pair up before they arrive at their breeding ponds.

Mating Frenzy. Many male toads will compete to mate with a female.

Photograph: Peter Stafford

year and the mortality rate at this time is extremely high, many hundreds being either devoured or just killed en-route by birds, cats, and rodents etc, or crushed by vehicles as the amphibians negotiate busy roads.

Spawning takes place in ponds, canals and ditches, always in fairly deep water. The males are the first to arrive and are followed by the females, some of which have already coupled with males which they have met on the way. Male toads make several croaking sounds, usually to each other during fights over the possession of females, although the actual 'mating call' itself is seldom heard.

In cold weather pairing may last a week or two but once actual spawning has begun the process rarely lasts more than twenty four hours. The eggs are laid in strings up to 3.5 metres in length with each string containing between 3000 and 4000 eggs in a double row. The amount of time taken for the eggs to hatch is dependent upon temperature but averages 12 days. Development of the larvae, or tadpoles, takes around two months. The fully grown tadpole measures a total length of 26 mm and the newly metamorphosed toadlet between 10 and 15 mm.

Hibernation generally begins in the middle of October but may be some weeks later if the weather is mild. Disused burrows of rodents may be utilized for the toad's winter sleeping quarters and large numbers of over 100 have been found in old rabbit warrens. Holes in walls, hollows beneath stones, or cavities between the roots of trees are also used or, alternatively, the toads will excavate holes of their own.

This species is regarded as being the most intelligent of the European amphibia.

NATTERJACK TOAD – *Epidalea* (formerly *Bufo*) *calamita*
(Running toad)

Identification: The natterjack toad is a comparatively small, robust species normally reaching from 45 to 80 mm although female specimens have been found occasionally at up to 90 mm in length. There is not a great deal of difference between the male and female and, with the possible exception of breeding time when the female is full of eggs, both are about the same size and have similar colour and markings.

Above, the natterjack is yellowish-green, olive grey, or brownish, and marbled with irregular brown spots. The underside is a dull yellow marked with brown and is usually very granular towards the vent. The skin is soft and covered with

The natterjack toad has been re-introduced to parts of Dorset.
Photograph: Tony Phelps

many flattish warts the largest of which are orange or reddish in colour. The pair of prominent, orange or yellowish glands (parotoids), one on either side of the head directly behind the eye, are small and straight, unlike those of the common toad which are large and crescent-shaped. There are also other large glands, one on each forearm and one on each of the lower hind limbs, which together are responsible for producing toxic secretions which act as a deterrent against predators.

The feature most characteristic of this species is the thin, bright yellow dorsal stripe of smooth, wart-less skin which runs down the centre of the back from the nostrils to the vent. This stripe may sometimes be greenish or even reddish in colour and in certain individuals it may be indistinct or absent altogether.

The breeding male natterjack has blackened excrescences (nuptial pads) on its thumbs, fingers and feet, which it uses to grip the female during the mating embrace, or amplexus, when spawning. Its throat, which turns bluish at breeding time, has an external vocal sac which is hardly noticeable when not in use but which can inflate, when the toad is calling, to the size of its head. The iris of the eye is a greenish-gold, unlike that of the common toad which is amber.

Longevity: The lifespan of this species is not known for certain but records of captive specimens indicate it reaches from 15 to 20 years.

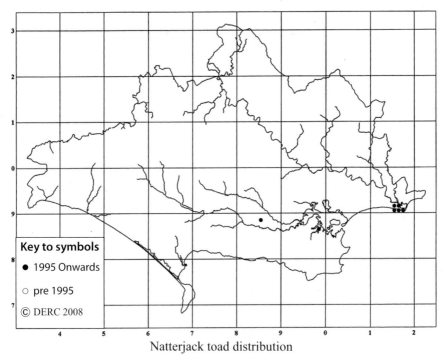

Natterjack toad distribution

Dorset range: Historic records seem to indicate that the natterjack toad was never plentiful in Dorset and it is thought that the last of any existing colonies finally became extinct in the county many years ago. In recent years however, there have been several successful attempts to re-introduce the species to certain suitable sites within the county, notably at Hengistbury Head in Christchurch, where it is doing extremely well and extending its range, and another on the edge of Poole Harbour. Work is continuing within the county to establish other sites for this rare and beautiful species.

Distribution in Britain: Whilst a few isolated colonies still exist in parts of Scotland, East Anglia, and Lincolnshire, the main stronghold of this species is now restricted to the coastal areas of north west England from Cheshire northwards to just within the Scottish border. The dunes of Merseyside and Cumbria account for over forty percent of the total British population. It is being reintroduced at suitable sites elsewhere. The natterjack toad is Britain's rarest amphibian.

Habitat: The natterjack toad prefers large expanses of infertile, sandy soils such as heaths and coastal dunes. Here it is able to live in self-excavated burrows, amongst short grass turf, heather and marram, close to shallow pools of brackish water in which it can breed. The species does not survive in pools in which the common toad is present.

Habits: Emerges from hibernation later than the common toad, reappearing in colonies at its breeding sites in late April or May. The males are the first to arrive and each night just before sunset they will sing in unison, attracting females from distances of up to two kilometres. The call of the male is a loud and persistent rasping, ratchet-sounding croak which is repeated two or three times at intervals.

The breeding pools are warm, shallow and unshaded waters, often in coastal areas and therefore quite brackish in quality. Once a male has located an unattached female he grips her around her armpits in a tight mating embrace and they may remain together in this way for a week or more until the eggs are laid. The female lays between 3000 and 4000 eggs in single cordons of spawn which may become snagged among the stems of submerged vegetation in the shallows. The adult

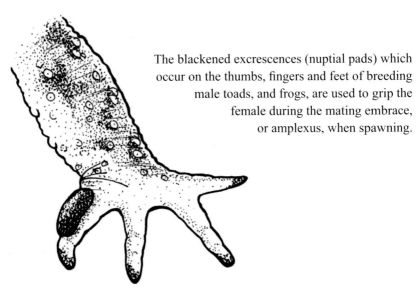

The blackened excrescences (nuptial pads) which occur on the thumbs, fingers and feet of breeding male toads, and frogs, are used to grip the female during the mating embrace, or amplexus, when spawning.

The toad's waxy skin helps it endure a dry, sandy environment.

females usually leave the pools immediately after spawning but the males generally remain.

Natterjacks often deposit their spawn in temporary pools which soon dry up as the summer progresses and this forces the larvae to develop rapidly. The eggs hatch after just 5 to 7 days and the dark reddish-brown larvae metamorphose in 5 to 8 weeks time compared to 10 to 12 weeks in the case of the common toad. The young toadlets measure some 6 to 9 mm when they emerge on to the land and are active mainly by day in order to prevent being caught and devoured by the more nocturnal adults and other night-time predators.

The natterjack's short, sturdy hind legs prevent it from hopping. Instead it moves in short runs although it can however leap up to 20 cm if suddenly alarmed or disturbed. It is on the whole a poor swimmer and apart from during the breeding season tends to stay away from water. It is on the other hand an excellent climber and can ascend almost vertical surfaces if it can find a grip with its strong fingers and toes. It is a very proficient burrower and will dig into damp, sandy soil, often at the very top of the vertical face of a dune amongst the roots of grasses and heather etc, up to a depth of between 30 and 50 cm. Here it will remain during the daylight hours. Its soft, almost waxy skin prevents the excessive loss of moisture and, consequently, it can withstand heat and drought extremely well.

This little amphibian has good eyesight and will actively pursue, and catch with the tongue, a variety of small animals including spiders, insects and their larvae, earthworms and other invertebrates. In October when the nights begin to get cooler it retreats into its burrow and within a few weeks will be in a state of torpor. It will remain in its burrow, safe from predators and the severities of the weather, until temperatures begin to rise once more in the following spring.

A whole colony of natterjack toads may suddenly uproot itself and migrate to a site elsewhere, often some great distance away. A population of this species, established at a particular location for a decade or more may for example, suddenly vacate the area and disappear, for no apparent reason, turning up at a place where they had previously been unknown. This, at first, seemingly odd behaviour may be due to different factors - their breeding pools may, over the years, have been drying out too quickly or they may no longer contain sufficient food for developing larvae. How these amphibians know where to go when they evacuate a certain locality is still somewhat of a mystery but these mass departures from customary sites may well be inherited: something natterjack toads used to do many many years ago in a time when their habitat was so vast it allowed them to move from place to place whenever they chose or when circumstances dictated.

Reptiles

SLOW WORM – *Anguis fragilis*
(Blind worm)

Identification: The longest of our native lizards attaining 300 to 400 mm. Larger specimens do turn up from time to time and a male found by the author on a Bournemouth golf course in 1989 measured 432 mm.

Males vary in colour from steel-grey to coppery brown above with a dark bluish-grey underside which may be unmarked or mottled with black. Older individuals may develop blue spots, which vary in both size and number, on their backs and flanks and although specimens of this form have been found in Dorset they are not common. The brick red to chocolate brown female has a distinctive narrow, dark stripe down the centre of its back and a black belly and flanks. Juvenile slow worms are a pale golden yellow, greenish, or creamy brown above while the underside and sides of the head and body are black. A narrow line (vertebral stripe), also black, runs along the centre of their backs from head to tip of tail. This stripe remains in females throughout their lives but in males it begins to fade during their second winter. Completely black, or melanistic, specimens have been recorded although infrequently.

The slow worm - an adult male.

The body of the male slow worm is long and slender compared to that of the female which is shorter and stouter. The length of the tail accounts for over half of the lizard's total length. The head is blunt and that of the male is larger and the neck consequently more defined. The scales are smooth and shiny and have a bright, polished appearance. They are larger on the upper surface than on the flanks.

The tongue, which is bluish-grey in colour, is not long and forked as in snakes but short and notched but, because the slow worm is limbless it is nevertheless frequently mistaken for a snake. Close examination of the head however reveals eyelids, features which are absent in all snakes.

Longevity: A specimen maintained in captivity in a Danish zoological museum reached an age of 54 years.

Dorset range: Widespread throughout the county.

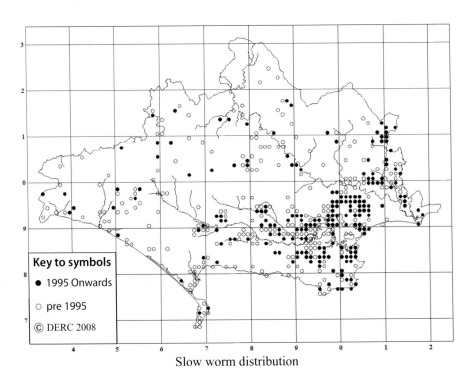

Slow worm distribution

Distribution in Britain: Found through England, Scotland and Wales although in certain areas, such as Lancashire, it may be rare or absent. It is absent from Ireland and the Orkney and Shetland Islands. It is the only reptile to be found in the Outer Hebrides.

Habitat: At home in a wide variety of situations including open heaths, commons, woodland clearings, parks, railway embankments and gardens. Also occurs in marshes and wet grassland but seems to prefer dry, well vegetated country with plenty of ground cover. In Dorset it is particularly abundant on the gorse-covered slopes and cliffs facing the sea between Swanage and Kimmeridge.

Habits: Except for during the breeding season, the slow worm is mainly crepuscular emerging to forage for food at dusk and dawn. Its prey consists of worms, insect larvae and spiders. Small snails are also taken readily once they have been carefully teased from their shells. Slugs, particularly the small creamy white slug *Agrolimax agrestis* are especially relished and are actively pursued and devoured. The slow worm drinks frequently but, although sometimes found near water, dislikes swimming and does so only if absolutely necessary.

The species is an excellent burrower and can move with surprising speed in light soils. On the surface it spends the daylight hours lying up beneath stones, log piles, sheets of corrugated iron and other debris and it is not unusual to find gatherings of up to 30 or 40 individuals - adults and juveniles - beneath such items. They dislike direct sunlight and retreat below logs or stones etc during the heat of the day, preferring to bask either early in the morning or in places where the sun's rays are filtered through vegetation.

An adult female slow worm.

Upper left: Old male slow worms may develop blue spotting.

Lower left: These blue spots on a mature male slow worm look like flecks of paint.

Upper right: When first handled the slow worm may attempt to tie itself in a knot.

Lower right: Although snake-like in appearance the slow worm possesses typical lizard features such as eyelids.

The slow worm hibernates below ground, sometimes several metres below the surface, often in large assemblies. Entwined 'balls' of over a hundred have been unearthed from time to time. Hibernation generally begins in October and lasts through the winter until late spring although it may emerge briefly if the weather is warm and sunny. During the hibernation period it survives on the fat deposits in its tail which it has built up during the summer months.

Depending upon prevailing temperatures hibernation usually ceases in April although it can come to an end as early as March. Males and juveniles are the first to emerge, females following some 2 to 4 weeks later. Males generally reach sexual maturity at the age of 3 and females at the age of 4 to 5 years.

Mating takes place between May and June and courtship can be quite rough, the male seizing the female's head or neck in his jaws and sometimes inflicting nasty lacerations as the two writhe about in their mating embrace. Rivalry amongst males is also intense at this time with much biting and wrestling going on between them. Larger individuals will seize smaller males in their jaws and hold on until they submit and leave the area. Fights to the death amongst males have been recorded.

Slow worms occur in many gardens throughout the county
where they feed on slugs and other invertebrate pests.

Once mating has taken place the slow worm concentrates on feeding and regaining its fat reserves after its long winter fast. Growth is usually rapid as the summer progresses and the skin is shed several times as the reptile grows.

As the embryos develop inside the gravid (pregnant) female she will bask frequently and, unusually for this species, often in the direct rays of the summer sun. She may at this time roll over on her side in order to expose her swollen belly to the heat, using her body as an incubator for the rapidly growing babies within.

The young are born in late August or September in membranous egg sacs (pellicles) which rupture almost immediately after they are expelled. Depending upon its size the adult female can produce anything from 5 to 20 young. There is no parental care and the young are fully independent the moment they are born. Young are between 60 to 90 mm in length at birth and grow rapidly often reaching 120 mm in the following 4 or 5 weeks before they enter hibernation and double that length by their second year.

The slow worm can lose its tail voluntarily (autotomy) when seized by that part of its body. This is a defensive action, causing the lizard no pain or discomfort, allowing it to escape safely. The wound heals quickly and a new tail grown later although never as perfect as the original. Specimens which have a stumpy, blunted tail have obviously lost one at some time.

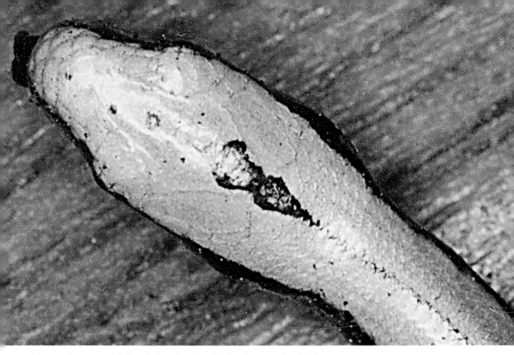

A baby slow worm's head showing the distinctive mark which
has caused them to be mistaken for baby adders.

A neonate (newborn) slow worm is barely bigger than a wedding ring.

COMMON LIZARD – *Zootoca* (formerly *Lacerta*) *vivipara*
(Viviparous lizard)

Identification: Adult specimens range from 85 to 170 mm with the comparatively thickish tail accounting for as much as two thirds of the total length. The markings may be extremely variable but the coloration is generally greyish, olive green, reddish brown, or almost black above. Adult males are generally darker on their backs which have scattered but well-defined pale-centred spots. Adult females are usually paler and frequently having a dark stripe, continuous or broken, down the centre of the back from head to base of tail with a broader stripe on each side edged with yellow or white streaks above and below, turning to spots on the tail. The smallish, rounded head is brown, sometimes with darker spots. Bright green individuals may occur occasionally and these may be confused with sand lizards in areas where both species are found. This green to an almost bluish colour is produced from an iridescence upon the scales and does not appear to be a pigment as in the case of the sand lizard so the colour and intensity changes depending on the light and angle of view.

In males the underside is yellow to deep orange and heavily spotted with black whilst, although in some populations of Dorset females it is orange, in most females it is yellow, grey, or pale blue with spots fewer or absent altogether. Completely black (melanistic) individuals may be encountered occasionally and these may not be uncommon in certain areas. Juveniles are dark bronze or black with two rows of paler spots down the length of the back.

A pair of common lizards (female below left). *Photograph: Peter Stafford*

Longevity: Records for the lifespan of this species have not been traced but six born and reared in an outdoor vivarium in 1971 reached ages averaging 8 years with one surviving 10 years.

Dorset range: Can be encountered, in suitable situations, over most of the county although its numbers in some parts seem to be diminishing, a factor due almost certainly to rapid and continual urban commercial development. The domestic cat may also be responsible for decimating small urban lizard populations, and other reptiles and amphibian species as well.

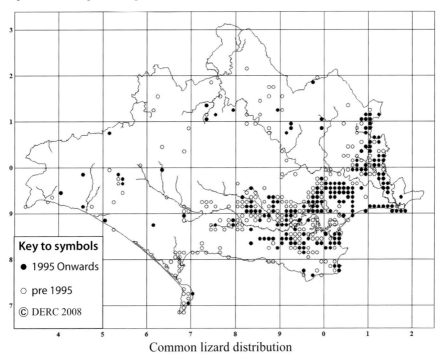

Common lizard distribution

Distribution in Britain: Occurs over most of England and Wales and is widespread over much of Scotland with the exception of the Outer Hebrides and a few Western Isles. It is the only reptile to be found in Ireland.

Habitat: Can occur almost anywhere although it seems to have a preference for areas with some dampness. Meadows, woodland clearings, marshy heaths, south-facing hillsides, dunes and even parks and gardens are all colonized by the common lizard. Railway embankments and sloping verges of motorways are also used with apparent disregard for noise and vibration and it sometimes occurs on the often sheer and salt-spray drenched cliffs around the coast. It is equally at home in areas with fairly sparse vegetation as it is in those with dense undergrowth.

Habits: The common lizard is one of the first of our reptiles to appear in the spring, sometimes as early as February if the weather is mild. Although it avoids great heat, retreating into shade or below ground during mid-day when the sun is at its hottest, it does like to bask on warm days for short periods. Certain individuals favour a particular basking place to which they will return day after day. The species is able to tolerate others of its own kind more so than some other reptiles and numbers may often be seen sunning themselves together. During basking the lizard's body is flattened and the legs extended with the soles upturned. In this position the lizard can receive as much heat as possible.

It is very active in pursuing and catching its prey and moves in a series of short runs pausing every few seconds to watch for movement in the herbage. Its hearing is extremely good and it will often track down an insect by sound alone. Food takes the form of small earthworms, insects and their larvae and spiders the

 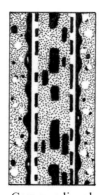 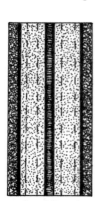

Sand lizard   Common lizard   Sand lizard

Diagramatic dorsal patterns.

largest of which are usually shaken against the ground and stunned first before being devoured. The wings and wing cases of some insects may be broken off and discarded before the remaining soft bodies are swallowed. Although the lizard obtains most of its water from the food it eats it will lap up droplets of rain or dew from leaves and stones etc.

The common lizard can swim well and readily takes to water whether in search of insects or in escaping from enemies. It is an agile reptile and although it is basically a terrestrial species it is an excellent climber and has been found on the tops of walls and clinging to fence posts and the trunks of trees. Radipole Lake in Weymouth, a reserve noted more for its birds, has a thriving population of common lizards and in late summer numbers of them, both adults and juveniles, can be seen sunning themselves up to a metre above the ground on the fences that line the reserve's pathways.

Common lizards often bask in small groups.

Courtship and mating takes place in April and May and the young are born alive some three months later, in numbers varying from 5 to 12. Measuring 25 to 35 mm at birth they are almost black in colour and are fully independent of their parents dispersing after a day or so into the surrounding undergrowth to fend for themselves.

The common lizard ranges further north than any other lizard species and occurs within the Arctic Circle. It is therefore comparatively resistant to cold weather and in Britain does not usually enter hibernation before November. The winter months are spent in a torpor below ground amongst the roots of trees, in old rabbit warrens or other suitable holes and cavities, sometimes in the company of other reptiles and amphibians.

As with the preceding species this lizard can shed its tail voluntarily if it is seized by that part of the body. This is purely a defensive action and within a short time the site of the fracture heals over and a new tail grows, although this is never as perfect as the original. A new tail can still be shed and any subsequent tails also but the point of fracture will always occur one vertebra up from the previous break. Some individuals have been found with two or even three tails regenerating from the site at which the original was detached.

The common lizard sloughs its skin as it grows. The process usually occurs some 8 to 10 times during the summer and, unlike that of snakes which generally comes off in one piece it is shed in small pieces over a period of hours or even days.

SAND LIZARD – *Lacerta agilis*

Identification: Compared with the common lizard this species is noticeably larger and more robust. The tail accounts for over half of the total length which is usually from 150 to 190 mm, exceptionally 220 mm. The coloration may vary considerably according to age, sex and habitat. Typical specimens are grey to light brown above with three longitudinal rows of dark brown spots, each with a central white spot, extending the whole length of the body. The top of the short and fairly deep head is brown or greyish. The flanks and belly of a mature male are green or yellowish green peppered with fine black spots. The flanks may also have a number of larger dark spots with whitish spots in their centres. During the breeding season the green colouring of the male becomes much brighter and more vivid. The adult female, whilst still being a handsome lizard, is usually not as colourful as the male being, in the main, greyish or brownish. The underside of the female is creamy white or pale yellow and the black spots found in the male are absent. In comparison to the common lizard the head of the sand lizard is heavier, especially in the male, and the snout blunter. The latter also has a pronounced band of narrow scales along the centre of the back and a greater number of dorsal scales (32-42) at mid-body compared to the common lizard (25-37).

A mature male sand lizard in breeding colours. *Photograph: Helen Fearnley*

Longevity: Records for the lifespan of this species have not been found but it is probably the same as that of other small lizards of the family Lacertidae, from around 8 to 11 years.

Dorset range: Dorset is now probably the main stronghold of this species in the British Isles with the densest colonies occurring in the east of the county. The areas in which the species is found are the heaths, acid grasslands, sand dunes, and sandy cliffs wherein the two most essential features are free-draining substrate and areas of open sand.

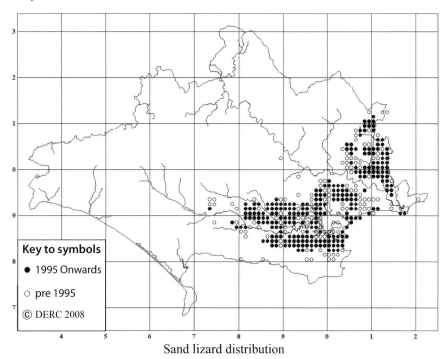

Sand lizard distribution

Distribution in Britain: A few populations survive in Devon, Hampshire, Wiltshire, Surrey, Kent and North Wales, and there is a small but dwindling colony on the Merseyside coast. Although small colonies exist in parts of Scotland and the coastal dunes of north west England the species is now almost entirely restricted to the southern sandy heaths of Dorset, Hampshire and the western borders of Berkshire and Surrey. Conservation efforts are currently underway to restore the sand lizard's range and boost its numbers elsewhere.

Habitat: This is essentially a species of dry, open, lowland country favouring sandy, well-drained heathlands and sand dunes. It can sometimes be found in meadows and woodland clearings, railway embankments, and on the golf courses of certain

Upper left: Despite lacking the vivid colours of the male, the female is no less attractive.
Photograph: Helen Fearnley
Lower left: A male and female will remain together during the breeding period.
Photograph: Helen Fearnley

Upper right: The female deposits her eggs in a shallow hole before covering them with sand.
Photograph: Tony Phelps
Lower right: The 5 - 8 oblong parchment-like shelled eggs hatch in August or September.
Photograph: Tony Phelps

seaside towns. Small colonies still survive on the cliffs between Bournemouth and Canford Cliffs, although these now seem to be suffering from the presence of the introduced wall lizard, and in some parts of the region, notably at Arne, it can be encountered on the beach.

Habits: An excellent burrower and although it spends a good deal of its time basking in the sunshine it dislikes great heat and during the hottest part of the day in mid-summer it will often retreat below ground in a hole which it has excavated for itself. It is most active in the late afternoon when it hunts for food in the form of insects and spiders. Large prey is usually shaken well before being devoured and large beetles and grasshoppers are frequently stripped of their wing-cases and legs respectively before being swallowed. The heads of certain flowers may be eaten from time to time and fruits also occasionally. Unlike the common lizard the sand lizard rarely climbs preferring to remain at ground level. It will however bask on the top of heather where it is well camouflaged.

Courtship and mating takes place in May and, less frequently, in June. Combat between rival males is common at this time and one which has secured itself a mate will fight and drive off all other males which approach. Copulation between the same male and female takes place repeatedly.

Oviparous, the female sand lizard lays from 5 to 13 tough, parchment-like shelled eggs in a shallow hole usually on a south-facing bank, covering them over with sand and small stones etc. The oblong eggs, which measure some 13 or 14 mm by 8 or 9 mm at first, hatch from 2 to 3 months later in August or September. On hatching the young are approximately 54 to 64 mm in total length and look very much like miniature versions of their parents but are paler in colour and have less well-defined markings. Their ocelli (eye-shaped spots) however, as individual as a human fingerprint, are quite distinct, distinguishing them from hatchling common lizards and remain with them throughout their life.

Although juveniles may remain in the vicinity of one another for a few days following their emergence from their eggs they soon disperse into the surrounding undergrowth. At the end of the autumn they average 80 mm in total length and by the following year they will average 130 mm in total.

The spots of a juvenile sand lizard are as individual as a human fingerprint.
Photograph: Tony Phelps

Hibernation begins in late September or early October depending upon the temperatures at the time. The holes and burrows that were excavated during the summer, as shelters from the heat and predators, are used as hibernating quarters and the disused burrows of rodents, holes in walls, and hollows amongst the roots of gorse and rhododendron are also utilised. (It has been found that although specific winter hibernating burrows are used annually, a number of different burrows may be used during the summer). Males seem to prefer to hibernate alone but females may spend the winter in small groups.

SMOOTH SNAKE – *Coronella austriaca*

Identification: A small and slender species seldom reaching more than 650 mm in length. Its scales are mirror-smooth giving it an iridescent appearance when in bright sunlight.

The ground colour is brownish-orange or reddish in the male and greyish in the female. A series of two, usually distinct dark brown spots run along the centre of the back and tail. These sometimes may be fused together to form bars, lines, or a combination of both on the same individual. Rows of smaller spots decorate the flanks. The top of the smallish head is dark brown with a darker, heart or crown-shaped mark at the rear, from which the scientific name *Coronella* originates. This head marking is frequently fused to the first pair of spots. The head and neck pattern, and size and shape of the spots, are peculiar to each snake and have been used to recognize individuals over a period of years. A dark streak starting at the nostril runs through the eye and along the side of the neck. The pupil of the eye is round in bright light.

The underside of the male is a mixture of pale orange and greyish-purple. The orange is particularly noticeable at the throat. The underside of the female is shiny black speckled with white near the throat. Young smooth snakes are darker than the adults with more distinct markings especially on the back of the head. Totally black, or melanistic, individuals also occur occasionally.

The smooth snake derives its name from its scales which lack keels.
Photograph: Peter Stafford

Longevity: The lifespan of this species is from 18 to 21 years although there are records of individuals exceeding 22 years.

Dorset range: The first smooth snake to be discovered in Britain in 1850, is generally accepted to have been a specimen, then unidentified, found on Dorset's Parley Common. Despite the fact that this is one of Britain's rarest animals it is nevertheless remarkably common in certain parts of the county (when compared with the status of other reptiles found in it). Healthy populations occur on many of the county's heathland blocks, including those within the conurbations, although the major populations are to be encountered in the established nature reserves particularly those at Studland and Arne in East Dorset, and on the older quarries where heath has regenerated after extraction.

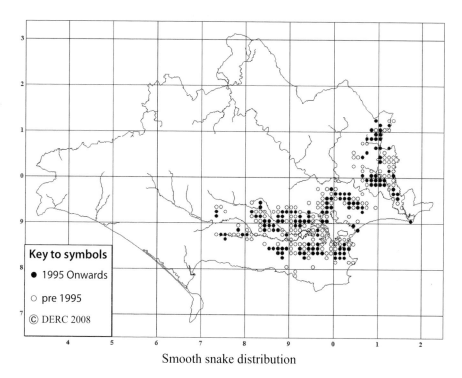

Smooth snake distribution

Distribution in Britain: Confined now almost entirely to a few of the sandy heaths in the south of England, namely Dorset, Hampshire and Surrey, although small numbers may still occur in certain areas in West Sussex, Berkshire and Wiltshire.

Habitat: Although the smooth snake has been found occasionally in or near marshy areas studies indicate it prefers well-drained sand heaths and woodlands.

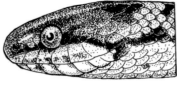

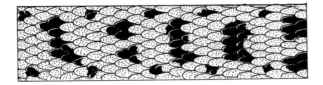

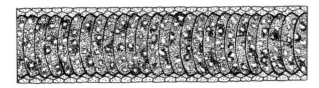

The smooth snake

Habits: Mating takes place soon after emergence from hibernation, in late March and April, but has been observed in late summer. There is often much fighting between rival males consisting mainly of 'wrestling' each other amongst entwined coils of their bodies. During intense fighting attempts to bite each other may take place and this sometimes results in one or more of the combatants receiving lacerations. Once a male has won a female mating takes place immediately. He grasps the female's head or neck in his jaws and entwines the rear of his body around hers so that their cloacae are aligned. As soon as sexual union has been engaged the two may remain thus joined for anything from 30 minutes to over 12 hours. Subsequent couplings may occur several times over the following days with the same male or, in some instances, with other males.

Extremely good at burrowing, the smooth snake spends a great deal of its time under loose soil. It dislikes hot sun and during the middle of the day it hides away under cover emerging again in the late afternoon to hunt for food.

Diet consists almost entirely of lizards although nestling shrews, voles and other rodents are taken when available. The common lizard is the snake's usual prey but it will also take slow worms and small sand lizards. The prey is seized between the jaws and one or two coils thrown around it. It has been said that the smooth snake does this to kill the prey by constriction. This is unlikely however as the victim is frequently swallowed alive. It is more probable that the snake uses its coils merely to subdue a struggling lizard and possibly to help it into its mouth. Young smooth snakes eat young lizards and may take certain invertebrates.

Smooth snakes copulating. The smaller, grey individual is the female.
Photograph: Tony Phelps

Although the smooth snake can move quite quickly when necessary its movements are generally casual and deliberate. If surprised or disturbed it will usually lie quite still for several minutes before finally slipping away into cover. If it is picked up however, it will very often hiss, bite, and release an earthy-smelling fluid from its vent similar to that of the grass snake but not quite so offensive.

Gravid (pregnant) females give birth in August or September to live young in litters varying from 4 to 16. They are born in transparent membranous sacs which soon rupture with the small reptiles' struggles. The lengths of the newly born snakes vary between 120 and 170 mm depending largely on the size of the adult female bearing them. They are able to live off the remains of fat reserves,

built up when they were embryos, for a long time and many will enter hibernation before they take their first meal and will start feeding the following spring some five months later. Growth is then fairly rapid and by the end of their first year they will have more than doubled in length. Sexual maturity is reached in the fourth year by which time they are around 500 mm in length.

Although the smooth snake has always been considered a reptile of dry, sandy heaths and woodlands, it nevertheless seems to have a great liking for water. It has been found on the fringes of marshes and appears to be especially fond of areas of *Molinia* tussocks below which there is water flowing horizontally but above which the surface remains dry in winter. During hot weather in mid-summer it will drink frequently and will often bathe for long periods when it will remain completely submerged except for its head. Despite its fondness for water it has never been known to devour fishes or amphibians.

The smooth snake enters hibernation in late October or early November depending on the temperature prevailing at the time. The winter months are passed in a state of torpor below ground, often in numbers, and ends when temperatures begin to rise again in March or April.

Above: Young smooth snakes soon lose some of the black on their heads, revealing the typical heart marking.

Above left: The common lizard is the smooth snake's usual prey. *Photograph: Tony Phelps*

Below left: Smooth snake neonates, or new-born. *Photograph: Tony Phelps*

Grass snake

Smooth snake

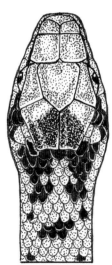

Adder

The heads of Dorset's snakes.

GRASS SNAKE – *Natrix natrix*
(Ringed snake; barred grass snake)

Identification: The grass snake is a strongly-built species and the largest of Britain's reptiles ranging in size from 700 to 1300 mm, although larger specimens as much as 1725 mm have been recorded. The tail accounts for approximately one fifth of the total length. Most specimens over a length of 900 mm are invariably females. Old females may be especially heavy and have large broad heads.

The ground colour is quite variable and can be olive-green, olive-brown, slate-grey or bluish-grey above, with dark brown or black markings in the form of bars at intervals along the flanks, and two rows of smaller dark brown or black spots arranged alternatively down the length of the back. The underside is chequered with black or grey, and white, often being completely black towards the tail, and the throat is off-white or pale yellow. A collar, characteristic of the species, is directly behind the head on and around the nape of the neck. This may be white, cream, yellow or pale orange in colour and is broken in the middle of the neck and bordered at the back by two fairly large triangular black patches.

The upper lip is white or pale yellow and the large scales around the mouth (labials) are divided with black. The scales on the upper (dorsal) surface and

The black and yellowish collar is generally a reliable identification feature.
Photograph: Peter Stafford

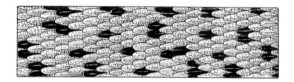

The grass snake.

flanks of the body are keeled. The pupil of the eye is round. Young specimens are somewhat darker and their markings less well-defined. Partial albinos of this species have been recorded.

Longevity: The species has been recorded as having lived, in captivity, for 20 years although there are unsubstantiated notes of it having lived for 26 years.

Dorset range: Although specimens can be encountered almost anywhere, particularly in gardens with ponds and water features, the grass snake's main presence in Dorset now seems to be limited, with a few exceptions, to marshy

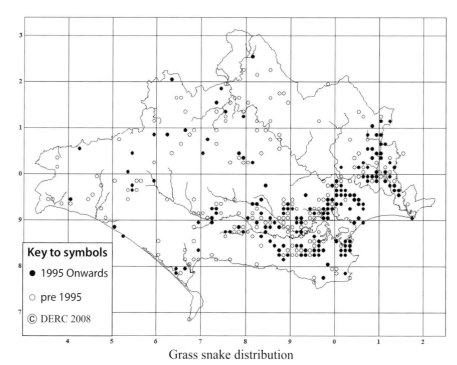

Grass snake distribution

locations within the region and, of all three snake species inhabiting the county, probably has the lowest population. The humid and marshy parts of the heathland areas between Shell Bay and Studland on the Isle of Purbeck are some of the best places for observing this beautiful snake.

Distribution in Britain: Found over much of England and Wales although it may be scarce or absent entirely in certain areas. Unconfirmed reports indicate it may occur in the south of Scotland and there are also records from near Edinburgh, although these may be the result of attempted introductions. The species is not found in Ireland.

Habitat: Woodlands, moorlands, heaths and meadows are all suitable habitats for this species although damp situations such as marshes and river banks are favoured most. However, it can be encountered regularly some considerable distance from water. It occurs frequently in both rural and suburban gardens, appearing in garden ponds throughout Bournemouth and Poole for example.

Habits: Active between April and October. Mating takes place in late April or early May and is preceded by a brief and simple courtship consisting of the male moving over the female in jerky movements while rubbing his chin on her back. His tongue is flicking in and out constantly during this activity. Once union

71

The pupil of the eye is round.

Typical death feint posture of the grass snake.
Photograph: Philip Pote

has been effected the pair may remain together in copulation for several hours. Matings have also been observed later in the year in August and September.

The grass snake rarely climbs but can do so well if necessary and sometimes crawls into small trees and low shrubs in order to bask or hunt for food. It is an excellent swimmer and spends a good deal of its time basking on the fringes of ponds and on the banks of streams and rivers etc, slipping silently into the water upon being disturbed without making so much as a ripple. It will dive frequently in search of food and can remain submerged for several minutes. When swimming on the surface it holds its head above the water.

Diet consists mainly of amphibians and fish but nestling rodents and, to a lesser extent, fledgling birds are taken when available. Lizards are also caught and devoured occasionally particularly in the drier areas in which amphibians are absent. The prey is seized in the jaws which are slowly worked over the body until it reaches the snake's throat where powerful muscles pull it down into the stomach. The grass snake has no means of killing its prey which is consequently devoured alive. Victims seldom struggle however, once they have been seized. Juvenile snakes will feed voraciously on small frogs and tadpoles, earthworms, and slugs.

The snake employs a variety of defensive tactics when threatened or disturbed. It will hiss loudly and will often strike repeatedly, though almost always with its mouth closed. Feigning death (thanatosis) is also used occasionally to confuse a predator: the snake rolls over on its back, its body becomes limp and still, its mouth gapes open and its tongue lolls out. If this fails to deter a potential enemy it will suddenly 'return to life', and thrash its tail around whilst discharging the contents of the anal gland in its vent. This fluid is extremely pungent and has a smell similar to garlic. It lingers for a long time on anything it comes into contact with and is commonly the grass snake's first line of defence.

The grass snake is our only snake species to lay eggs. These are laid in a clutch, varying in number from 10 to 50 depending upon the size and age of the female, in June or July. They measure about 25 mm long by 15 mm across and have a tough, parchment-like shell. They are usually deposited in damp soil, holes in walls, or beneath dead or rotting vegetation. Compost heaps or piles of grass cuttings are often used, the heat and humidity being generated by them aiding the incubation of the eggs. The eggs, which grow in size as the embryos develop, hatch after 40 to 46 days in late August, September or early October.

The hatchlings measure between 150 and 200 mm and are immediately ready to lead independent lives. Although they may remain at the nest site for a day or two they soon move off into the surrounding countryside. Sexual maturity is reached in their third or fourth year.

In October or November, depending on the temperature, the grass snake retreats into hibernation in disused rabbit warrens, beneath the roots of trees or in holes in walls, and it is not unusual for numbers to hibernate together, often in the company of other reptile species.

ADDER – *Vipera berus*

(Northern viper; crossed viper; common viper)

Identification: A small but comparatively heavily built species attaining an average length of between 450 and 550 mm. Females grow larger than the males and sometimes reach lengths of over 600 mm.

Extremely variable both in colour and markings with no two individuals being identical. Ground colour can be silvery-grey to creamy white, olive, yellow, red, reddish-brown or dark brown. Albino specimens have been found and completely black specimens occur also, the latter being more common in some areas than in others.

The markings are generally black, dark grey, red or dark brown. A characteristic and strongly defined zigzag stripe on the back extends the length of the body from neck to the tip of the tail. In rare specimens this may appear as a straight, broad stripe. Also, a line of irregularly sized, round or oval spots run the length of the body on each side.

The underside is dark grey, brown or black, often dappled with lighter spots. The extreme tip of the tail is reddish or yellow. On the back of the head is a V-shaped mark, the apex of which points towards the snout. In some individuals

Male adders can vary from white to yellow and brown to olive but always have dark grey or black markings.

this mark may form an X. Completely black specimens usually show some signs of the characteristic pattern and have a reddish patch on the throat.

The adder's body is comparatively thick and heavy and more broad than high. The tail is short and accounts for approximately one sixth of the snake's total length in the male, and an eighth of the total in the female. The neck is narrow and the flat head is lozenge-shaped and almost arrow-like, being broad at the base and tapering towards the snout. Unlike the eyes of the smooth and grass snake, which have round pupils, the adder's are cat-like and close vertically in bright light. The iris is copper coloured. The scales on the upper surface of the body are strongly keeled.

This species is one of the few to exhibit sexual dimorphism, or a difference between the sexes. Males are generally silvery-grey, off white, yellowish, or olive with dark grey or black markings, and the females gold, reddish or brown, with dark red or chocolate brown markings.

Longevity: Reliable records indicate this species can reach in excess of 20 years.

Dorset range: Although it may occur only locally in some parts, the adder is the commonest snake in Dorset and can be found, in suitable habitats, almost anywhere within the county.

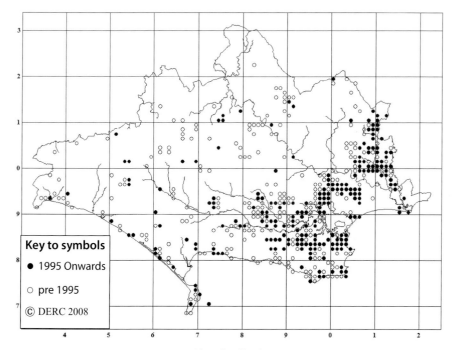

Adder distribution

Distribution in Britain: Distributed fairly widely over England and Wales and, apart from one or two isolated populations of possibly introduced grass snakes, is the only snake to occur in Scotland. Whilst locally abundant in some areas it may be scarce in others. It is declining rapidly in the Midlands and indeed may now be extinct in some counties. It is most numerous in southern and north-eastern England and in certain areas of central Scotland. It is absent from the Orkneys, Shetlands, Outer Hebrides, Isle of Man and Ireland.

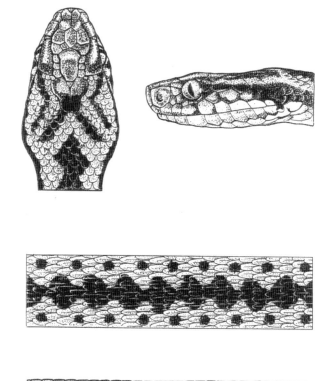

The adder.

Above left: A female adder is usually brown or reddish but
    always wth chocolate brown or red markings.
Below left: A black, or melanistic adder. *Photograph: Tony Phelps*

Upper left: The markings on an adder's head usually take the form of a 'V' or an 'X'. *Photograph: Chris Gleed-Owen*

Lower left: The adder's pupils are eliptical and cat-like in bright light.

Upper right: Brown female adder.

Lower right: Red female adder.

Habitat: May be encountered in almost any type of habitat and is equally at home at sea level and on the slopes of the highest hills. Although found in damp situations it seems to prefer drier terrain with a thick ground cover of gorse, bramble or heather etc.

Habits: The adder is the only snake species found within the Arctic Circle and can therefore withstand the cold more than our other reptiles. It has been seen basking on thawing snow and in recent years has been observed as early as New Year's Day.

The males are the first to emerge from their hibernation quarters and, after a few days, slough their skins and take on a bright, fresh appearance. The females emerge some 14 to 20 days later and mating takes place as soon as the weather is warm enough, usually in April. The males have frequent disputes with one another at this time and indulge in combat over prospective mates. This ritual consists of chasing each other with the front halves of their bodies raised vertically in the air. It is essentially a contest of strength and none of the combatants ever use their fangs on each other. They twist and twine about one another, each trying to wrestle

78

Above: Yellow male adder.

Below: Grey male adder.

Two male adders in ritual combat.
Photograph: Tony Phelps

the other to the ground. Such fights, or 'dances' as they are known in some parts, may last from a few minutes to over an hour. The winner takes possession of the female.

Most active in the early morning and late afternoon, the adder basks for an hour or two at sunrise. However, like most reptiles it dislikes great heat and during the middle of the day when the sun is at its highest and hottest it seeks the cool shade and shelter of the undergrowth emerging once again an hour or two before sunset. It is often seen more on a warm and overcast day than on a hot and clear day. The author has found that on particularly hot days it will retreat below ground or beneath stones, fallen trees and other debris and venture forth in the evening to continue its activities throughout the night (Wareham, 1998). In coastal areas the adder actually appears to like heavy sea mists and has also been observed moving about in light drizzle. Outside the breeding season it has a comparatively small territory and the same individuals can be seen often within the same few square metres day after day during the summer months.

The diet of the adder takes the form of common frogs, common lizards, slow worms, small mice, voles and shrews and, sometimes, nestling birds, all of which are killed by the snake's fast-acting venom. It does not as a rule hold on to its prey

Copulation between adders generally takes place in thick vegetation.

Above: A female adder may lose over half her body weight giving birth.

Below: Baby adders are born in transparent membranes from which they break out a short while later.

Below opposite: A juvenile adder having recently fed. *Photograph: Peter Stafford*

but bites and lets go, hunting the victim down some minutes later when the venom has taken effect. Combat, similar to that employed during courtship, may take place over a particular prey item and can be indulged in by male against female, female against female, and even by juveniles. In such cases the strongest usually gets to eat. In rare instances, if two adders get a hold on the opposite ends of the same animal the larger of the two may well end up eating not only the animal but the other adder as well.

The young are born some 4 to 5 months after mating, in August or September, and number from 5 to 16. Like the smooth snake, the adder is ovoviviparous and the young are born fully developed inside transparent membranes from which they break out almost immediately after birth. They slough their skins for the first time soon after birth and are immediately capable of independent existence, equipped with fully- operational fangs and venom. They are some 150 to 200 mm in length. It is possible, sometimes, to sex newly born adders by their colour but most are usually reddish in colour and markings. They don't normally take on the colours of the adults until their second or third year. Sexual maturity is reached at 4 to 5 years of age.

Because of its comparatively short and stocky build the adder is not particularly good at climbing. It will, however, enter shrubs and low trees in the search for prey or to seek tangles of branches through which it can crawl when sloughing its skin. The author has observed adders coiled in the branches of a fallen silver birch and looking very much like strange fruits ripening in the early morning sunshine.

Like all snakes the adder can swim well but does so infrequently and reluctantly. Should it find itself in water it will make every attempt to get out as quickly as possible.

Hibernation normally begins in late September and early October in holes in the ground, under fallen trees, in quarries and in the conduits beneath man-hole covers. In recent years, with our increasingly mild winters, adders have still been active and above ground in late November. Large numbers may spend the winter months together and over 40 have been uncovered, indicating that they travel over some distance to a particularly favourable hibernation site. Snakes born in September may go straight into hibernation without having fed. These will live off fat reserves laid down when they were embryos and they may even grow a little as the winter progresses.

On the whole the adder is quite a secretive reptile, usually slipping away unnoticed and only defending itself when trapped or provoked. Many farmers, for example, who have worked their land day after day for many years, have sometimes been quite unaware that they have a colony of adders inhabiting their hedgerows and meadows.

Because its colouring and markings help the adder to blend so well into its surroundings, a small number of people do get bitten accidentally each year, usually when picking flowers or walking barefooted over heaths and dunes. Fortunately the bite is rarely fatal, just twelve deaths occurring during the whole of the 20th century, although symptoms are sometimes unpleasant. Of course, as with any animal bite, it is always prudent to seek expert medical advice in the unlikely event of being bitten.

The venom of the adder is one of the mildest of all the vipers.

A WORD ABOUT THE ADDER

Although a small number of people receive bites from adders every year, fatalities are very rare indeed (the last recorded death was in 1975) and, in the majority of cases, those who suffer most are the elderly, children, and people who are in ill health. The chances of being bitten are extremely slim but, in the unlikely event of an accident one should know how to deal with it.

Most bites occur on the feet, ankles and hands and the majority of these are a result of people interfering with, or deliberately aggravating the snake. Immediate symptoms are usually, but not always, a burning pain and swelling at the site of the punctures. These symptoms may however not manifest themselves for over an hour. The swelling in some cases spreads up the whole limb and is often accompanied by discoloration of the skin. Depending largely on the general health and fitness of the victim, the development of further symptoms may or may not occur and, if they do, can vary in their severity. In some cases the symptoms may be nothing more serious than minor discomfort whilst in others they may be slightly more alarming with sickness, diarrhoea and, sometimes, even loss of consciousness.

Over the years many forms of treatment have been advocated. These have varied from the drinking of large quantities of alcohol to the cutting of the flesh around the bite and the application of potassium permanganate crystals into the wound. Both of these and the many other 'home remedies' can have disastrous, if not fatal, results and should never be attempted under any circumstances.

It has been suggested, by a number of authorities, that probably the best, simplest, and safest way of treating the bite of an adder is to immobilise the affected limb, with a splint or sling if possible, in order to slow down the movement of the venom in the bloodstream. A tourniquet is not advised as the concentration of the venom within the affected hand or foot by application of such a stricture increases the extent of local tissue damage and the possibility of death of tissue (gangrene) in severe cases. The victim should be kept warm and rested with constant reassurance that everything is going to be all right whilst professional medical aid is sought.

In extremely rare cases a victim of an adder bite may develop a hypersensitive condition known as anaphylactic shock. This is a severe, often frightening, potentially life-threatening allergic reaction that occurs in certain people who have developed an extreme sensitivity to a particular substance (allergen). Introduction of the allergen, in this case adder venom, into the bloodstream results in the release of huge amounts of histamine and other chemicals that affect the tissues of the body. Blood pressure suddenly falls severely as the blood vessels widen and other symptoms such as abdominal pain, swelling of the tongue or throat, and constriction of the lung's airways, may also occur.

A person showing signs of anaphylactic shock will become severely ill or collapse soon after being bitten in which case *urgent medical attention should be sought immediately*. In the meantime the victim should lie flat with legs raised to improve the flow of blood to the heart and brain. An injection of adrenaline can often mean the difference between life and death in such circumstances and should be administered as soon as possible.

Certain individuals are sensitive to the serum that is part of the antivenom and it can be this rather than the actual snake venom that causes anaphylactic shock, especially if the person has had previous injections of serum that may cause sensitization. Steroids and antihistamine have also been used to treat the bite of the adder. As with the bite of any animal, bacteria that may be present on the fangs of the snake can cause serious problems, so it is always advisable to have a course of antibiotics following a bite.

It must be stressed that the venom of the adder is one of the mildest of all the vipers and in the majority of cases is no worse than a bee sting. In fact more people die from bee stings than they do from adder bites. The severity of the bite can depend on several factors: the adder may only puncture the skin with one fang thereby only administering half of its venom; it may recently have bitten a small animal and most of its venom may therefore have been temporarily expelled; or it may puncture the skin with both fangs but not inject any venom at all. The site of the bite is also crucial in whether or not symptoms develop. A bite over a bone, such as the ankle bone or knuckle of a finger, is likely to be less troublesome than if it were in soft flesh where the fangs could penetrate deeper.

Obviously the chances of receiving a bite are higher if an adder is provoked, or handled in a careless manner, or if one goes walking through long undergrowth in inadequate footwear. Where handling this species is concerned even the most experienced herpetologists have been bitten so, unless one is fully aware of the risks involved, this species should be left well alone and observed only from a distance.

For the many of those who like to explore the countryside on foot to look for reptiles and other wildlife it really seems hardly necessary to point out that strong footwear, preferably boots of some kind, is essential. Some form of long, tough trousers and a thick pair of socks will help to protect the legs not only from tears and scratches caused by the undergrowth but also from the jaws of the adder should one be stepped on accidentally.

Opposite: A female adder. Bites from this species are rare and usually occur only by accident or when it is meddled with.

ESCAPES, INTRODUCTIONS AND MISCELLANEOUS VISITORS

In recent years it has become increasingly evident that a growing number of people are releasing their 'exotic' pet animals into the countryside when they find they can no longer care for them. This illegal practice is causing much concern amongst naturalists and conservationists, for the introduction of any creature alien to these shores can have a detrimental effect on our native flora and fauna.

In the past, numerous deliberate and controlled attempts have been made to try and establish populations of 'foreign' reptiles and amphibians here in Britain. The reasons behind these endeavours have not always been clear. Surely, it has been argued, it would be far better to try and safeguard what we already have, rather than expend such a great deal of time, money, and energy, and with such uncertain conclusions, into projects introducing species which we either never had in the first place, or which became extinct, naturally, years ago.

Most of the 'aliens' have been unable to tolerate our temperate climate and have failed to reproduce, eventually perishing during a particularly hard winter. Nonetheless, certain introduced species, such as the wall lizard *Podarcis muralis*, Aesculapian snake *Zamenis longissima*, midwife toad *Alytes obstetricans*, alpine

A male wall lizard. This species has only recently taken up residence in Dorset.

Upper left: A female wall lizard.

Lower left: A juvenile wall lizard is completely at home on vertical surfaces.

Upper right: The green lizard is quick to defend itself against any threat.
Photograph: Chris Gleed-Owen

Lower right: An adult male green lizard.
Photograph: Peter Stafford

newt *Mesotriton alpestris*, edible frog *Rana esculenta*, and European tree frog *Hyla arborea*, for example, have adapted reasonably well to the British weather. Small populations of these are in fact actually thriving in certain parts of the British Isles although, to date, of all these 'foreigners' only the wall lizard and a species of green lizard, *Lacerta bilineata* (formerly *viridis*), have actually colonised parts of Dorset.

The author well recalls a particular colony of green lizards (species unknown) living on the then sandy, heather-clad, south-facing slopes of Constitution Hill, overlooking the harbour and town of Poole, between 1959 and 1962. These were large, robust, vividly-coloured, and relatively aggressive lizards, quick to open their mouths at any threat. This aggression did not, however, stop the entire colony from being completely decimated within just a couple of summers by teenage boys from a local secondary modern school.

The bright green reptiles, up to 40 cm in length, were dug from their burrows beneath the heather, with anything from gardening trowels to dessert spoons.

The lizards were then taken back to the boys' suburban homes where they were housed in totally unsuitable containers such as old galvanised baths, goldfish bowls, and biscuit tins, poked and prodded to encourage them to show their aggressiveness, and offered woodlice, snails and earthworms as food. Needless to say, none of the lizards are thought to have survived.

In the case of the wall lizard, an attractive and lively species reaching some 23 cms in length, there have been somewhat scattered and, to some extent, erratic and largely unreliable records in the county although a seemingly well established colony has inhabited a solitary limestone quarry on Portland for some years. Other colonies now appear to be thriving further eastward on the Purbeck coast and again on a stretch of cliffs at Poole Bay and Bournemouth where they entertain passers-by with their agile activities on the zigzag paths and walls. The species is also to be found at Shoreham and just across the water on the Isle of Wight.

How and when these colonies of 'alien' lizards came to be in these locations in the first place, no one can really say and unless someone actually comes forward and admits to releasing them we will probably never know the answer. The author has wandered the cliffs between Poole and Hengistbury Head, observing and recording the reptiles on them, since 1966 and although seeing numerous common lizards, sand lizards, and the occasional slow worm over a forty year period, did not record his first 'probable' wall lizard, on the cliffs at Bournemouth, until 1992. At the time, because the lizard was only glimpsed fleetingly, it was dismissed and recorded as having been *"either an observational error or an unusually marked common lizard"*. Subsequent visits however, confirmed that a number of wall lizards were indeed inhabiting the cliffs there.

Also around the mid-1990s sightings of the larger green lizard at another site further along the cliffs at Southbourne, were being reported. Since then both species have been seen regularly although, at the time of writing, the wall lizard would appear to be the most numerous of the two.

So, how did these species come to establish themselves at these sites on the south coast? It is most likely they either escaped accidentally from one or more private collections or, perhaps more probably, were deliberately released. They could well have been freed by individuals who could no longer keep them as pets. There were, after all, several dealers in the region at the time selling these species. Or they may simply have been innocently released by those who had collected them on their European holidays thinking they would brighten up their gardens back home. Whilst some would say both the wall and green lizards make very attractive additions to our fauna, others are rightly concerned that they are competing with our already endangered resident sand and common lizards over both territory and food.

Above left: A female green lizard. *Photograph: Chris Gleed-Owen*

Below left: Juvenile green lizards. *Photograph: Chris Gleed-Owen*

Of all the varied species of animals to be abandoned in the local woods, streams, and lakes, those most frequently discarded seem to be, by all accounts, reptiles and amphibians. And right at the top of the list is the red-eared terrapin.

The red-eared terrapin *Trachemys scripta elegans* is a native of North America and, over the years, many hundreds of thousands have been imported for sale as pets, the majority of them coming into the country as hatchlings not much bigger than a fifty pence piece. The species has an average lifespan of 40 years and, with correct diet and conditions, can reach 280 mm in length (the size of a dinner plate) in just a few years.

Public enemy number one - the red-eared terrapin.

The introduction of any animal, whether deliberate or accidental, can upset the natural balance of a particular ecosystem. For this reason, if any person releases or allows to escape into the British countryside any animal which is not normally a resident or a regular visitor in a wild state they will now be guilty of an offence under Section 14 (1a) of the Wildlife and Countryside Act of 1981.

Despite the Act however, the red-eared terrapin is beginning to appear regularly in many parts of Britain. In Dorset some 63 different sightings of this reptile were brought to the author's attention in 2000. In the following year this number rose to 87, and in 2002 it increased to 98. In 2005, sightings of this alien reptile rose to 127. Other sightings probably went unrecorded or were reported elsewhere. Anglers nationwide have found them on their hooks and, in several areas, although much of the field work on this species shows that most of the

Above left: The red-eared terrapin can reach the size of a dinner plate.
    Photograph: David Bird
Below left: Nowadays one is more likely to see a terrapin than a water vole.
    Photograph: Philip Pote

adults seem to be almost completely vegetarian, terrapins have been blamed for a drop in the fish populations of certain canals and lakes. Indeed the situation has become so bad in some areas that the chances of seeing a terrapin are now higher than those of seeing a water vole.

As well as the deliberate releasing of reptiles and amphibians alien to our shores there is also a rather worrying increase in accidental releases. In these cases animals are obtained from pet shops or garden centres with the innocent intention of stocking the garden pond. No problem there, one might think. The pond is, after all, on private property. However, most amphibians, including seemingly completely aquatic ones, such as the African clawed frog *Xenopus laevis*, leave the water at certain times and venture forth to seek food, mates, or new territories. Unless the garden is completely enclosed it is inevitable that these amphibians will find access to the surrounding countryside eventually.

Amphibians most commonly introduced into garden ponds include the alpine newt *Mesotriton alpestris*, Italian crested newt *Triturus carnifex*, marbled newt *T. marmoratus*, and the sharp-ribbed salamander *Pleurodeles waltl*. These four species probably do not occur in sufficient numbers, at the moment, to pose any threat to our native species although the marbled newt and the larger sharp-ribbed salamander may well compete for food in waters which they share with native newts.

The African clawed frog and the American bullfrog *Lithobates* (formerly *Rana*) *catesbeianus*, the latter of which was often available as tadpoles, do pose a threat however. Both have voracious appetites, as larvae and as adults, and will overcome and devour anything that they can cram into their mouths including our native reptiles and amphibians. If the presence of either of these two species is suspected in any of Dorset's waters the matter should be reported, as soon as possible, to one or more of the addresses listed elsewhere in this book.

The keeping of exotic reptiles and amphibians is a very popular hobby and many people are now breeding and rearing a whole range of these fascinating and beautiful animals in their own homes. Even the most careful keeper experiences 'losing' one of his captives now and then and as more and more people come into the hobby so the instances of escapes are increasing. The majority of these 'escapees' never actually succeed in getting outside the confines of the owner's home and are usually recaptured in a matter of hours. Of those that do manage to make it outside most are soon recovered nearby. Others either perish with the cold or in the jaws of cats or dogs, or are crushed beneath the wheels of vehicles.

The small number which remain unaccounted for may well survive for many months if they can find shelter and sufficient food. Some may even breed and establish stable populations, as has been evident with the midwife toad in Bedford, the Aesculapian snake in North Wales, and now the green lizard and wall lizard in Dorset. At present the problem seems to be confined to just three or four species in three or four localities but this could well change in the future. Bearing in mind how our climate is changing, if we scan the list of species currently offered by dealers and consider the most extreme scenario, who knows what we may find one day on our heaths and in our woodlands.

MISCELLANEOUS VISITORS

Of the seven species of marine turtle distributed throughout the oceans of the world, some are now making the epic journey to British waters from tropical shores in unprecedented numbers. Sightings of the green turtle *Chelonia mydas*, the loggerhead turtle *Caretta caretta* and Kemp's ridley turtle *Lepidochelys kempii,* one of the rarest species with a world population of just a few thousand, have increased by over 20 percent in the past 20 years. The huge luth or leatherback turtle *Dermochelys coriacea*, the largest of all the chelonians, also often appears during the summer months, mainly in the Irish Sea and western isles but also around the south and south-west coasts, having followed the Gulf Stream in pursuit of its favourite food, jellyfish.

Once again, as global temperatures rise and the sea around our coasts becomes warmer so the chances of seeing one or more of these magnificent marine reptiles increases greatly. Dorset is already seeing an increase in other marine creatures from warmer water, such as sharks, dolphins and certain fishes, so it is always worthwhile watching out for turtles whilst walking along the cliff tops or taking a boat trip.

Finally, a brief mention must be made about the 'illegal immigrants'. Each year numbers of reptiles and amphibians enter the country illicitly, as stowaways in the holds of ships and aircraft, hidden in consignments of machinery, timber and cereal, amongst fruit and vegetables, and even in the luggage of unsuspecting travellers.

Such stowaways are almost always discovered on, or soon after, arrival and are usually taken away for identification and proper care and attention by R.S.P.C.A. officers or staff from the nearest zoo.

Most of the amphibians that arrive in this way are small tree frogs of various species. Their small size and adhesive toe pads enable them to travel unseen, attached to the insides of crates and other containers. Whilst some arrive emaciated and close to death others arrive in the best of health obviously having fed prior to or during their journey.

The majority of the reptiles which enter the country as stowaways are small lizards such as anoles and geckos. Like the tree frogs these lizards are equipped with adhesive pads on their toes which means they can secrete themselves in the smallest of spaces in almost any position, even upside-down if necessary.

Snakes also travel hidden amongst the cargo although not as frequently as frogs and lizards. Those that do are usually small individuals which, like the others, enter crates and containers which are awaiting processing at their points of departure. Examples of illegal snake immigrants are the slender rough-green snake *Opheodrys aestivus*, a metre in length, which turned up in a consignment of plants at an East Dorset garden centre in 1989, and the small, venomous Asian pit viper which arrived in a box of fruit in 1992.

Although the majority of these stowaways are usually accounted for, some almost certainly slip away unnoticed when cargoes are unloaded at their destinations. One can only guess at what happens to them afterwards. In a busy place, such as Poole Harbour for example, they face numerous hazards, from being run over on the roads to being caught and devoured by a host of predators. A variety of suitable and inviting habitats are but a stone's throw away however and it is not unreasonable to think that, sooner or later, one or more of these illicit immigrants, perhaps laden with fertile eggs, will establish themselves there.

WHAT THE FUTURE HOLDS

The heathlands of north-west Europe, with their dazzling yellow gorses and rich purple heathers, were at one time thought to be of natural origin. It has since been discovered however, that heaths were created artificially.

Around 6000 years ago our lowland heaths that we walk today were almost certainly covered by an ancient wildwood of species such as oak and hazel, growing in nutrient-poor, often sandy soil. As Bronze Age farmers began clearing these forests so the formation of our heaths began. Once cleared of tree cover, the poor-quality, shallow soils could no longer support crops so the land was turned over to rough grazing by cattle, sheep and ponies. The heathland which thus became established was maintained by subsequent generations by the continuation of stock grazing, and the cutting of heather turves and gorse for fuel and bracken for bedding.

Heathland quickly becomes invaded by pine, rhododendron, bracken and birch scrub. When, and if, this is left unmanaged it eventually becomes woodland again. The novelist Thomas Hardy depicted the 'blasted heath' as a place of desolate and austere beauty but it has, unfortunately, always been looked upon by many as a worthless sterile wasteland.

Dorset is now almost certainly the stronghold of the sand lizard, one of Britain's rarest animals.

Dorset as a whole has lost almost 90 per cent of all its heaths in less than 200 years, mainly through improvements to grassland, conversion to farmland, afforestation, and building developments. Since the 19th century huge tracts have been devoured by expanding towns such as Bournemouth and Poole whilst other areas have been isolated and fragmented by road construction. The county is now left with some 7000 to 8000 hectares of what are the most important European examples of this unique and rare habitat.

The Dorset countryside, and in particular that of the Purbecks and Poole Harbour, has been and continues to be at the centre of some of the most urgent planning and conservation issues. In 1988 the World Wide Fund for Nature expressed publicly its concern about the Dorset heathlands. This surprised many members who thought the WWF should be giving priority to national and international issues rather than local ones. What they failed to realise was that the Dorset heathlands are of both national and international importance and fully deserving of more attention than the WWF could afford to provide. It was exactly because the future of the heathlands had been treated as a local issue that many of the problems had arisen.

Today practically all of the county's heathland areas are nature reserves and most of these have received protection with Site of Special Scientific Interest (SSSI) status. Added to which some areas have now become Special Areas of Conservation (SACs) under the EU Species and Habitats Directive. The aim of the Directive is to conserve the 169 habitat types and 623 species currently (at the time of writing) identified in its Annexes I and II and requiring a succession of high quality SACs to be established throughout Europe.

Ironically, much of Dorset's countryside and wildlife is being threatened, albeit indirectly in many cases, by the very people who purport to enjoy it. As more people move into the county so the demand for more homes and bigger and better roads increases. It is a region under constant pressures from visitors, necessitating more camp sites, more hotels, and bigger car parks. At present, people are visiting the county to see the beautiful scenery but, if the situation is not kept in check, it might not be too long before much of that scenery is either irrevocably ruined or, in some cases, destroyed completely, with only new homes and new roads remaining.

Coupled with these obvious threats and poor or incorrect management, there are the more subtle ones such as problems that are sometimes caused by self-sown pine, fly-tipping, fires, gravel and clay extraction, and erosion from unsupervised and unauthorised motor-cycle scrambling, mountain boarding, and mountain biking, to name just a few. Some of the threats such as rural and urban development are irreversibly damaging. Others though may not be completely destructive, at least in the short term.

Afforestation for instance may leave open, heathery ride edges suitable for wildlife including reptile populations, and tree crops may fail enabling reptile colonies to survive on planted heathland. Also when, in the case of gravel extraction

Heathland can quickly become invaded by pine, rhododendron, bracken and birch scrub.

for instance, the surface layer of gravel has been removed and the sand layer allowed to regenerate as heathland, its populations of reptiles, especially colonising species such as the sand lizard, may then be larger than that of pristine mature heath. But these are all maybes and maybe is not acceptable when discussing the destruction of habitats and the likely disappearance of animals.

The increasing number of fires, both accidental and deliberate, continues to cause much concern. The controlled rotational burning of heather and gorse has been practised for a number of years at certain sites, partly because young gorse bushes provide nest sites for birds such as the stonechat and rare Dartford warbler and partly to lessen the threat of damaging uncontrolled fires.

Whilst fire is a natural part of heathland development and regeneration, too many in the wrong places, such as those on municipal fringes for example, can be extremely harmful. Not only do such fires destroy many plant and animal communities they also allow invasive species such as birch, bracken and rhododendron to take hold, resulting in the eventual smothering or shading out of other heath species. When a particular area is degraded in this way, thereby losing much of its scientific interest, there is a real danger that it will cease to be designated an SSSI. This then leaves it wide open for development.

A lot of heathland fires have been, and continue to be, blamed on children as they often seem to occur during school holidays. As a consequence, Natural England and local authorities are now working closely with the police and fire services to tackle the growing problem of fires by placing particular emphasis on education.

One should however, not be too quick to point the finger at young people, most of whom have nothing but the greatest respect for their environment. On the other hand, many adults who, for instance, have a 'commercial interest' in undeveloped land, are only too aware of the fact that protected areas can lose their protection when degraded by damaging fires, thus leaving them ripe for housing and retail development.

Organisations such as the British Herpetological Society, the Herpetological Conservation Trust, the Dorset Wildlife Trust, Natural England, and the Royal Society for the Protection of Birds are working hard to clear important reptile and amphibian sites of bracken, pine and scrub. Also, in a number of areas, farmers are being encouraged to allow some of their previously cultivated land to be turned back to heathland.

In the largest single scheme, within an umbrella project called Tomorrow's Heathland Heritage, the Heritage Lottery Fund, Natural England (formed in October 2006 by the merger of English Nature, the Countryside Agency and the Rural Development Service) and a dozen other conservation bodies are together funding a nationwide restoration project committed to a four- to five-year cycle of scrub, heather and bracken management on our remaining lowland heaths as well as restoring some 7000 hectares. The Dorset Heathland Project, set up by the Royal Society for the Protection of Birds and the Ministry of Defence, has already restored more than 1,000 hectares of heathland in the county since 1989.

Many areas of the county are protected with Site of Special Scientific Interest (SSSI) status.

Just because an area had been declared an SSSI did not unfortunately, until recently that is, mean that everything on or in it was safe and secure. Since 1985 over 500 such sites have been damaged or destroyed. Strangely enough the various conservation organisations had been powerless to act in many cases because they could not force management agreements, thereby appropriating supervision, on to owners and occupiers of SSSIs. Such agreements could only be imposed when an owner or occupier wished to undertake a 'potentially damaging activity'. Now though, some twenty five years on from the angry disputes between environmentalists and landowners over the 1981 Wildlife and Countryside Act, Natural England

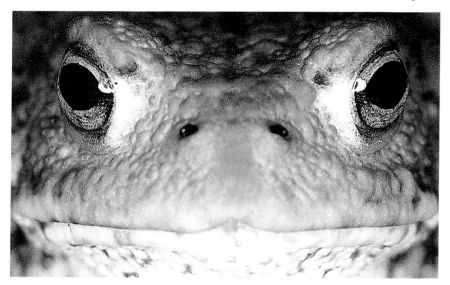

The common toad, a casualty of the modern world and sadly
no longer as common as its name would suggest.

finally has the power to protect privately owned SSSIs. Under the Countryside and Rights of Way Bill, introduced in March 2000, Natural England will now be able to impose management notices on landowners for mismanagement and neglect, and decline approval for any damaging management activities. Should deliberate damage be inflicted on an SSSI a subsequent prosecution could result in a fine of up to £20,000 in the Magistrates Court and unlimited fines in the Crown Court, with a court order to restore the damaged site to its original condition.

Finally there is that other, new threat, not only to our lowland heaths and their often unique and rare plants and animals but to our countryside as a whole; one that will almost certainly affect our reptiles and amphibians - climate change. Experts inform us that whilst some parts of the country may receive less rainfall and even experience drought conditions, the heavy, prolonged and record-breaking rainfall experienced in 2000 and more recently during the summer of 2007 is likely not only to get worse but also more commonplace in certain areas in the years to come. Floods resulting from such exceptional rainfall will undoubtedly have an adverse effect on our flora and fauna, especially our frog, toad, and newt populations if and when, for instance, ponds, lakes and streams overflow and either wash their amphibian communities down the drains or disperse and strand them in places totally unsuitable for their survival.

Milder winters, also predicted, may well mean that hibernation could be either interrupted, or maybe even abandoned altogether by some species, which in turn could dramatically affect their breeding cycles and reproduction, and hotter, drier summers could result in the gradual disappearance of important wetland areas upon which several of our reptiles and amphibians currently depend. In addition, rising sea levels could, in the long term, see the permanent inundation of low-lying habitats currently important to reptiles, and other fauna and flora.

There will, no doubt, be many debates on this fairly recent revelation and how it can be overcome, if indeed it can be, in the months ahead. In the meantime, the many towns and villages of Dorset, eager for both social and economic growth, are on the point of overflowing and engulfing the last remaining, already fragmented, examples of the internationally important habitats which surround them.

The Government recently forecast that there will be over 55,000 new homes built in the county of Dorset by the year 2011. The South West Regional Assembly (SWRA), which advises the government on how many homes should be built in the region, has greatly angered planners by demanding a great deal more housing than the planners say is sustainable. Between now and 2026, for example, the SWRA is demanding 190 new homes a year to be built in Christchurch, 270 a year in East Dorset, 545 in Poole, and a staggering 880 a year in Bournemouth. (Bournemouth's target includes an average of 50 homes a year on the town's already shrinking green belt).

There are going to be a great many pressures on Dorset in the years to come, many problems to be faced, and many questions to be answered. We can only hope that the solutions to these are favourable to all concerned, not only to the reptiles and amphibians but to all the communities of plants, animals and people who share this beautiful county.

REPTILES, AMPHIBIANS AND THE LAW

In the past many snakes, particularly the adder, have been deliberately killed, either out of ignorance or fear, resulting in the depletion of local populations. Consequently snakes are now uncommon in certain areas and even extinct in others where they were once quite abundant. Frogs, toads, newts and lizards suffered severely as their fragile habitats were systematically destroyed in the name of progress, and the numbers and distribution of all our native species experienced further decline as the collection of these animals for the pet trade added to the problem.

It soon became obvious that legal protection was necessary if these and certain other animals and plants were not going to disappear altogether. On 1 August, 1975, a total of 21 plants and six animals came under the protection of the law. The six animals included the natterjack toad, sand lizard and smooth snake. Except in certain circumstances or under license it became an offence to take, injure, kill, sell or offer for sale any of those creatures. The reference to 'sell or offer for sale' also included the skeletons and skins of dead specimens. None of the protected animals could be kept in captivity except under licence.

It was not long before it was realised that the remaining British reptiles and amphibians, as well as many other animals and plants, would have to receive

A juvenile natterjack toad.
This species cannot be handled without a licence.

some degree of protection also. In 1981 the Conservation of Wild Creatures and Wild Plants Act, as it was then known, was reviewed and became the Wildlife and Countryside Act. Besides the three species just mentioned, the great crested newt was also awarded full protection with the remaining native reptiles and amphibians enjoying either protection against deliberate killing or injuring and, or, at least a ban against the trade or offering of those species for sale (except under licence).

The Wildlife and Countryside Act 1981 is a lengthy document setting out comprehensive statutory protection for endangered wild species and their habitats. The Act is amended periodically and new legislation can come into force at any time. To keep up to date with any possible new legislation one should write to the *Department of the Environment, European Wildlife Division, Room 902, Tollgate House, Houlton Street, Bristol BS2 9DJ.*

In certain circumstances licences may be issued for special purposes such as scientific or educational activities, ringing or marking, photography, and translocating specimens to other areas for example, but the licensing of these activities is not a straightforward matter. Anyone who thinks they may require a licence for such purposes is advised to contact the appropriate agency. For use in the county of Dorset one should apply to Natural England who also cover the rest of England.

New legislation came into force on 30 October 1994 entitled 'The Conservation (Natural Habitats, etc.) Regulations 1994 implementing the Council Directive 92/43/EEC (the Habitats Directive) in the UK'. The Wildlife and Countryside Act 1981 remains the main UK conservation legislation but certain differences now apply to species which are covered by both the Act and the Habitats Directive. This includes for example it being 'an offence to disturb an animal', as opposed to 'disturbing an animal while it occupies a place of shelter'. The additional protection afforded by the Habitats Directive relates to the great crested newt, natterjack toad, sand lizard, smooth snake and all five marine turtle species.

Unless one does have a special and valid purpose in mind it is perhaps better not to attempt to catch any of our reptiles and amphibians, protected or otherwise. Our lizards lose their tails readily if held incorrectly and, although they grow back later are never as perfect. All are nervous creatures and are subject to stress when captured or confined and, because they are comparatively small and delicate, are obviously susceptible to injuries if treated roughly or carelessly. Both snakes and lizards can break bones if allowed to slip from one's grasp and fall to the ground, and the heat from a human's hands can quickly burn the delicate, moist skins of amphibians.

All the various Acts of Parliament relating to the protection of wildlife and the countryside are usually available in most local or university libraries or can be obtained from Her Majesty's Stationery Offices.

Opposite: The persecution continues. This adder was beaten, decapitated, and impaled on a barbed wire fence.

WATCHING REPTILES AND AMPHIBIANS

When to watch

Spring is almost without doubt the best time for watching both amphibians and reptiles. Vegetation is generally low and at its most sparse at this time making it fairly easy to spot these animals as they begin to appear after emerging from hibernation. The fact that temperatures are still on the low side means also that they, snakes and lizards in particular, are not quite so quick to disappear into cover and can therefore be approached and observed more easily.

Depending on the prevailing weather conditions reptiles and amphibians can begin to appear in Dorset as early as the beginning of January. Frogs, toads and newts often carry on most of their activities under the cover of darkness but any time from February to April they can be found during the day in and around their breeding waters. Because the breeding instinct is so intense they can be watched usually without too much difficulty from the banks of ponds and lakes as they search for mates and spawn. Although they are often oblivious to anything else it is a good idea to keep as low a profile as possible particularly on a clear day if they are not to suddenly dive to the bottom and hide amongst the water weeds. Newts are a little more difficult to watch because they are smaller and do not engage in mass spawnings. They also usually do their courting and spawning on the

A male wall lizard on cliffs at Bournemouth.

bottoms of ponds and streams so unless the water is shallow, clear and ripple-free they may not be seen until they rise to the surface to take air.

The adder can be seen frequently laying out amongst the grass or on bare sandy patches almost anytime from January onwards. If the weather is cold they will often be coiled up tightly but as the weather warms up they will spread themselves out more in looser coils. The females emerge from hibernation a short time after the males and if one is lucky the ritualistic fights between males contesting a female can be witnessed. Common lizards and sand lizards are also easier to get closer to at this time and can be seen in places they are known to frequent warming themselves in the spring sunshine.

As the year progresses and temperatures start to rise so the vegetation starts to grow and reptile and amphibian watching becomes more of a challenge. The newts, frogs and toads, spawning now over, disperse and move off into the surrounding countryside and now, possibly, may only be found by accident more than anything else either by accidentally disturbing one whilst out walking or discovering one beneath a stone, log, or some other debris.

Our snakes and lizards must have warmth in order to function proficiently but too much and they can overheat. Warm temperatures with an overcast sky and little wind are ideal conditions for seeing reptiles at any time throughout the day. During the middle of a clear day however, when the mid-summer sun is at its strongest, they usually seek shelter and cooler temperatures and can then become almost impossible to find. In such conditions it is best to look for them in the early morning between 06:30 and 10:00 hours and again in the late afternoon between 15:00 and 20:00 hours.

Where to watch

Different species have different preferences with regard to the type of areas they inhabit and readers should familiarise themselves with these preferences by studying the species accounts elsewhere in this book. It has to be remembered though that an area which looks to be a typical example of ideal snake or lizard habitat can actually be completely devoid of any reptile life at all. This is commonly the case when a habitat has become fragmented and when fires may have destroyed the reptile population and colonization has been unable to occur from adjacent areas. Conversely, they can often turn up in the most unexpected and unpromising-looking places.

Becoming familiar with the favoured habitat of a species and getting to know its particular habits and food requirements will go a long way in helping to recognise which sort of terrain is likely to prove fruitful and which is not.

Reptiles and amphibians are, on the whole, shy and retiring animals. Most species are likely therefore to avoid areas in which there is a lot of activity, human or otherwise. There are always exceptions to every rule though: the small colony

Above: A fragment of sloughed skin from a sand lizard. *Photograph: David Bird*

Below: An adder's sloughed skin. Such skins are excellent evidence that a particular species is present in a particular area.

Upper left: The landward side of sand dunes can be home to sand lizards and adders.

Lower left: Stone walls, rock piles and quarries can be good for several reptile and amphibian species.

Upper right: Although adders have very distinctive markings they can still be very difficult to spot in tangled undergrowth.

Lower right: Basking amongst the heather a sand lizard is superbly camouflaged and can be easily overlooked.

of adders, discovered by the author in 1995, living around the perimeter of a busy Purbeck caravan park; a colony of natterjack toads which, in the summer of 1991, were running around between the feet of holiday makers in an area of sand dunes on the Merseyside coast; and wall lizards which have, seemingly, become so habituated to human activity they now sun themselves and hunt for food on walls and paths within a metre or so of people going to and from a Bournemouth beach.

Whilst inside any area which has been designated a reserve it is very often necessary, if not essential, to keep to the sign-posted paths and boardwalks. Outside of the reserves however it often pays to wander a little way off the beaten track. Here the chances of spotting a basking lizard or snake increases greatly. Be mindful at all times of course that it is currently illegal to disturb our four rarest species: the natterjack toad, great crested newt, sand lizard and smooth snake.

Take great care to respect the countryside and not to trespass on private land or damage the habitat in any way. Although most of our heathlands now have a right of public access and are designated 'Open Access Land' it is nothing less than courteous to ask land owners' permission if in any doubt. It should also of course always be remembered that despite the fact that many such parts of Dorset are indeed now 'Open Access Land' they have also been designated areas important for wildlife at both a UK and European level.

Stone absorbs heat easily so dry-stone walls therefore are always worth examining. Such constructions provide ideal shelter and basking sites for lizards and snakes. Walking the length of one that borders a field for example will often reveal common lizards, a slow worm or two, and perhaps even an adder. Rock piles too provide refuges for both reptiles and amphibians. Consequently, quarries can be extremely rewarding places but one should of course always be aware of the dangers of exploring such sites.

South-facing banks and hills with plenty of ground cover such as mature heather, gorse and bramble are good places to start looking for species such as the adder, common lizard and slow worm. The landward side of sand dunes too can be good for adders as well as the sand lizard. Those readers who also enjoy the game of golf should keep an eye open next time their ball goes in the rough. Many of the county's links courses have communities of all three lizard species, and the smooth snake, grass snake and adder have occurred from time to time on some. Those courses which have water obstacles such as ponds, lakes and streams, can also be home to frogs and toads.

The common, sand, wall, and green lizards slough, or shed, their skins several times during the course of the summer. As in most lizards the skin is shed in pieces and although many species eat the skin as it is sloughed it is still possible to find fragments amongst the vegetation. Snakes also shed their skin several times in a season but usually in one piece. Beginning at the head it is slowly rolled off turning inside out as it does so. Such complete sloughs or skin fragments are excellent evidence that reptiles are present at a particular site.

How to watch

When watching any kind of wild animal stealth, silence and patience are essential. These qualities are just as important, if not more so, if one is to see reptiles and amphibians with any degree of success or regularity.

Learn to walk softly. Lizards have acute hearing and snakes, which are deaf to most air-borne sounds, can pick up vibrations through the ground. Vibrations will also travel quickly and easily through water so taking care to tread lightly when walking on the banks of a river or pond will improve the chances of seeing amphibians or snakes which may be dwelling there.

On bright sunny days always try, if possible, to walk in a direction so that the sun casts your shadow behind and not in front of you. Whilst walking scan the ground from left to right in an arc and from between one and three to four metres in the direction of travel.

Finally, try not to break the horizon. For example, either attempt to approach a likely looking spot by going around rather than over a hillock or mound or, if this is not feasible, keep as low a profile as possible by stooping or even crawling if necessary.

Many snakes and lizards, if suddenly frightened, will disappear into the undergrowth only to return five or ten minutes later to the same spot once they think the danger has passed. If a specimen is thus disturbed accidentally, sit down quietly or stand motionless nearby and it may well emerge again entirely unaware that it is being observed.

A pair of close-focusing binoculars is a useful item of equipment. By sitting down at some concealed vantage point, courting lizards, a snake shedding its skin, and spawning frogs can be watched in breath-taking detail with them. Consequently, with a little care and a lot of trial and error, one can eventually develop the field craft necessary for watching these fascinating and beautiful creatures at a respectable distance so that they remain completely undisturbed throughout.

They are of course not going to be seen on every walk in the Dorset countryside. Days can go by and many miles walked without seeing a single specimen even though the conditions appear to be just right. In these situations though one can at least simply enjoy being in what is undoubtedly some of the most beautiful scenery in the British Isles.

DORSET'S NATURE RESERVES

Many of Dorset's reserves are managed by organisations such as the Royal Society for the Protection of Birds, Natural England, and the National Trust. The Herpetological Conservation Trust and the Dorset Wildlife Trust are also responsible for the management of an extensive series of reserves in the county. All of these bodies, as well of course as the various county and district councils, do vital and sterling work in helping to protect the communities of varied and often unique plants and animals, reptiles and amphibians included.

Dorset has many nature reserves, both local and national.

Some of the more important reserves, as far as reptiles and amphibians are concerned, include Arne (SZ 063931), Hartland Moor and Stoborough Heath (SY 945855), Studland Heath (SZ 030845), Alder Hills (SZ 063931), Townsend (SZ 024782), Avon Heath Country Park (SU 125039), Tadnoll (SY 792873), Wareham Forest (SY 905895), Hengistbury Head (SZ 175907), and Sopley Common (SZ 132975).

Access to some reserves, or to parts of them, may be restricted at certain times of the year or may be allowed only by permit. The necessary permits, together with further information about the reserves and the flora and fauna they hold, can be obtained by writing to the following addresses (*opposite*):

112

Natural England (Dorset Office)
Slepe Farm
Arne
Wareham
Dorset, BH20 5BN
(www.naturalengland.org.uk)

Dorset Wildlife Trust
Brooklands Farm
Forston
Dorchester
Dorset, DT2 7AA
(www.dorsetwildlife.co.uk)

Royal Society for the Protection of Birds
The Lodge. Potton Road
Sandy
Bedfordshire, SG19 2DL
(www.rspb.org.uk)

The Herpetological Conservation Trust
655A Christchurch Road
Boscombe
Bournemouth
Dorset, BH1 4AP
(www.herpconstrust.org.uk)

National Trust
Eastleigh Court
Bishopstrow
Warminster
Wiltshire, BA12 9HW
(www.nationaltrust.org.uk)

Visitors to the nature reserves should follow the country code at all times:
- Keep to the designated paths,
- Keep dogs under close control, especially near grazing stock,
- Protect the wildlife, plants and trees, and
- Guard against all risks of fire.

Anyone who would like to join in the important work of helping safeguard Dorset's wildlife should contact the Dorset Wildlife Trust's office at the above address. New members are always welcome.

PLACES TO VISIT

Reptiles and amphibians are normally somewhat secretive in their habits and, as a result, tend to seek out places where they can remain unseen. They are, as a result, not easy animals to display in captive environments. It is for this reason, and the fact that they can spend up to five months of the year in hibernation, that most zoos tend to exclude them from their collections. There are, however, a few establishments, especially in southern England, that do display some, if not all, of the British species during the summer months, and are worth a visit if one wants to have a closer look at these fascinating and beautiful animals.

A trio of sand lizards. *Photograph: Helen Fearnley*

Important breeding colonies of the rare natterjack toad and sand lizard are housed in spacious outdoor enclosures at *Marwell Zoological Park, Colden Common, Winchester, Hampshire SO21 1JH (Tel: 01962 777407)* where they are bred in numbers for re-introduction and population-boosting schemes elsewhere. In order to keep disturbance to a minimum, these landscaped and predator-proof enclosures are not on show to visitors although they may be viewed by prior arrangement.

With the possible exception of the natterjack toad, all of our native reptiles and amphibians can be seen at the *New Forest Reptile Centre (Tel: 023 8028 3141)* approximately two miles west of Lyndhurst on the A35 Bournemouth Road and open from April to September between 10:00 and 16:30 hours. Furthermore, some of our native amphibians and all three of our snakes are sometimes on view at the *Zoological Society of London, Regent's Park, London NW1 4RY.*

Marwell has spacious enclosures for the rare sand lizard . . .

. . . and natterjack toad. *Photographs: Tim Woodfine*

CLUBS AND SOCIETIES

There are many herpetological societies and clubs in the British Isles. Whilst two or three have international standing the majority are regional and have a more local appeal. Some concentrate mainly on the husbandry and breeding of captive species whilst others deal chiefly with field research and conservation of wild species. Each responds to the needs and interests of both professional and amateur herpetologists by offering a means of gathering and distributing all the latest information through its various newsletters, journals, monographs and other publications. Regular meetings enable members to discuss their relevant interests with like-minded enthusiasts of all ages and from all walks of life.

The details of the main organisations, particularly where the British reptile and amphibian species are concerned, are listed below, along with that of a fairly recently formed and important Dorset group. Details of the others can be obtained from county museums, libraries and zoological gardens.

> *The Herpetological Conservation Trust (HCT)*
> *655A Christchurch Road*
> *Boscombe*
> *Bournemouth*
> *Dorset, BH1 4AP*
> *(www.herpconstrust.org.uk)*

> *The British Herpetological Society (BHS)*
> *c/o The Zoological Society of London*
> *Regent's Park*
> *London, NW1 4RY*
> *(www.thebhs.org)*

> *Dorset Amphibian and Reptile Network (DARN)*
> *c/o The Herpetological Conservation Trust*
> *655A Christchurch Road*
> *Boscombe*
> *Bournemouth*
> *Dorset, BH1 4AP*
> *(www.herpconstrust.org.uk)*

Opposite: Common frogs. A familiar sight in many garden ponds.
Photograph: John Wareham

POSTSCRIPT

All snakes are without external ears and are, in principal therefore, 'deaf' to most air-borne sounds. Instead they depend largely on their capability to sense, through their bodies - certain bones of the lower jaw in particular - vibrations which are transmitted through the surface on which they lie. If a snake is basking in the summer sun it will 'feel' the footsteps of anyone approaching and quickly disappear into the undergrowth, usually without ever being seen. Only if it is surprised, trapped or provoked will it naturally respond by hissing and, on occasion, attempting to strike.

If a snake is encountered whilst out walking in the countryside, stand still and take the opportunity to look at it. Should it be blocking progress and it becomes necessary to move it, stamp a foot or strike the ground with a stick but please . . . do not strike the snake!

The grass snake. *Photograph: Peter Stafford*

FURTHER READING

Appleby, L. G. *British Snakes.* John Baker, 1971.

Arnold, E. N. and J. A. Burton. *A Field Guide to the Reptiles and Amphibians of Europe.* Collins, 1978.

Arnold, H. R. *Atlas of Amphibians and Reptiles in Britain* (Institute of Terrestrial Ecology research publication No 10) HMSO, 1995.

Ballasina, D. *Amphibians of Europe.* David and Charles, 1984.

Beebee, T. and R. Griffiths. *Amphibians and Reptiles.* HarperCollins, 2000.

Cambridge, O.P. *Coronella laevis Boie.* Proceedings of the Dorset Natural History and Antiquarian Field Club 7, 83-92. 1885.

Cambridge, O.P. *Reptiles of Dorset.* Proceedings of the Dorset Natural History and Antiquarian Field Club, 15, 90-102. 1894.

Corbett, K. *Conservation of European Reptiles and Amphibians.* Helm, 1989.

Cullingford, C. N. *A History of Dorset.* Phillimore, 1980.

Dalton, R.F. *A Preliminary Re-survey of the Distribution of the Dorset Amphibia & Reptilia: with some notes on their characters and habits* Proceedings of the Dorset Natural History & Archaeological Society, Vol.72 135-43. 1950.

Dorset Environmental Records Centre. *Mammals, Amphibians and Reptiles distribution maps. Present state of recording in Dorset.* D.E.R.C, 1980.

Fitter, R. S. R. *Reptiles and Amphibians in Britain.* Collins, 1983.

Gent, A. H. and Gibson, S. D. (Eds) *Herpetofauna Workers' Manual.* Joint Nature Conservation Committee, Peterborough, 1998.

Griffiths, R. *How to Begin the Study of Amphibians.* Richmond Publishing, 1987.

Leighton, G. R. *The Life History of British Lizards.* Morton, 1903.

Lever, C. *The Naturalised Animals of the British Isles.* Hutchinson, 1977.

Phelps, T. E. *Seasonal Movements of the Snakes* Coronella austriaca, Vipera berus *and* Natrix natrix *in Southern England.* British Journal of Herpetology Vol. 5, No. 11, 755-761. 1978.

Prestt, I. *An Ecological Study of the Viper,* V. berus, *in Southern Britain.* Journal of Zoology 164: 373-418. 1971.

Riddell, A. (Ed) *The Slow-worm.* British Herpetological Society, 1997.

Simms, C. *Lives of British Lizards.* Goose and Son, 1970.

Smith, M. A. *The British Amphibians and Reptiles.* Collins, 1973.

Steward, J. W. *The Snakes of Europe.* David and Charles, 1971.

Wareham, D. C. *Notes on the Nocturnal Activities of the Northern Viper,* Vipera berus, *in Southern England.* British Herpetological Society Bulletin (63) 27-31, 1998.

Webb, N. *Heathlands - A Natural History.* Collins, 1986.

Further information on the flora and fauna of Dorset can be obtained from:

Dorset Environmental Records Centre
Library Headquarters
Colliton Park
Dorchester
Dorset, DT1 1XJ

Dorset County Museum
High West Street
Dorchester
Dorset, DT1 1XA